Secret Firearms
An Illustrated History of
Miniature and Concealed Handguns

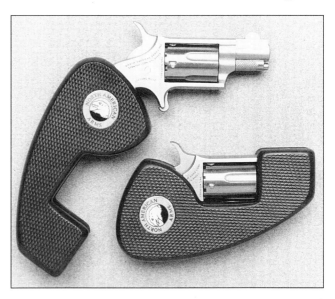

The .22-calibre North American Arms 'Mini-Revolver' is little more than a modernised Suicide Special, though undeniably very well made. The folding grip – by no means a new idea – provides a thought-provoking carrying method, even if the projecting hammer spur still poses a threat in the pocket.

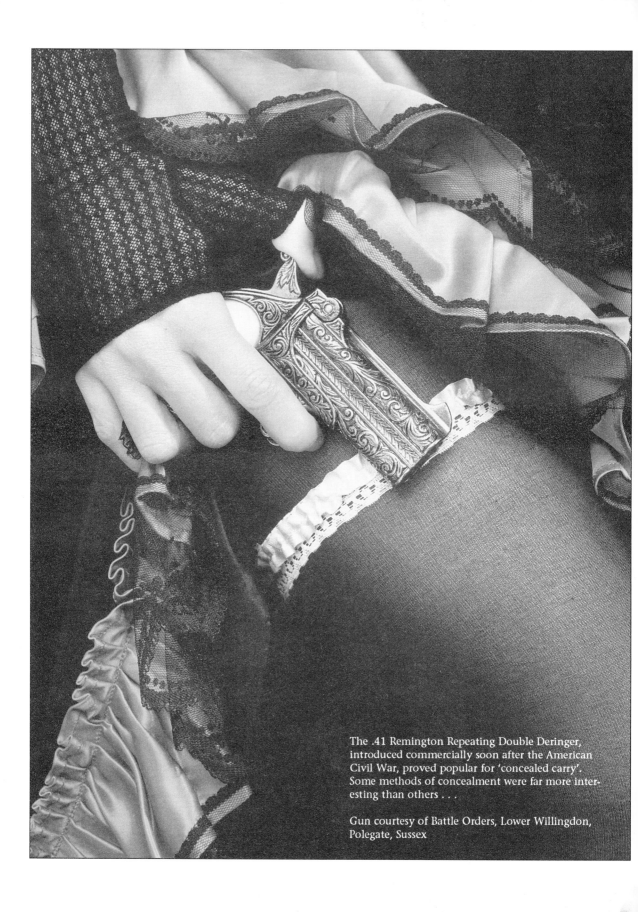

The .41 Remington Repeating Double Deringer, introduced commercially soon after the American Civil War, proved popular for 'concealed carry'. Some methods of concealment were far more interesting than others . . .

Gun courtesy of Battle Orders, Lower Willingdon, Polegate, Sussex

SECRET FIREARMS
An Illustrated History of Miniature and Concealed Handguns

JOHN D. WALTER

ARMS AND
ARMOUR

For Ally, Adam and the Menagerie, with love

AUTHOR'S NOTE

Secret Firearms presents the concise story of concealed, disguised and compact pistols and revolvers. It does not specifically cover true miniatures – e.g., sixth-scale Winchester rifles or pistols which are the size of a small coin. These have no real defensive value, even though many are capable of being fired.

I would like to thank the enthusiasts who have contributed to the project. There are many accessible sources of information, but I must acknowledge a special debt to Anthony Taylerson's books on the revolver, J. Howard Mathews' monumental *Firearms Identification* project, the work of Aleksandr Zhuk (*The Illustrated Encyclopedia of Handguns*), and many of the excellent articles published over the years in *Gun Collector's Digest*.

The sources of illustrations are credited individually in the captions, but (in particular) I would like to thank Ian Hogg, Frederick Wilkinson and Joseph J. Schroeder for help above and beyond the call of duty.

John Walter, Hove, England, 1997

Arms and Armour Press
An Imprint of the Cassell Group
Wellington House, 125 Strand, London WC2R 0BB

Distributed in the USA by Sterling Publishing Co. Inc., 387 Park Avenue South, New York, NY 10016-8810.

© John D. Walter, 1997

British Library Cataloguing-in-Publication Data:
a catalogue record for this book is available from the British Library

ISBN 1-85409-230-8

Designed and edited by DAG Publications Ltd. Designed by David Gibbons; layout by Anthony A. Evans; edited by Philip Jarrett; printed and bound in Great Britain.

CONTENTS

PROLOGUE

The emergence of the handgun could never have happened without suitable propellant, which probably derived from the incendiary compound known colloquially as 'Greek Fire'. An appropriate mixture of pitch, charcoal, fat and sulphur would undoubtedly have spluttered and flared. Even though this was not truly explosive, it is easy to understand how a particular mix could have been ignited with great force when confined – and how the first steps towards a true explosive were taken.

GUNPOWDER

The geographical origins of gunpowder are no longer known with certainty. Much credit is usually given to an English Franciscan monk, Roger Bacon (c.1214–92), who, in 1242, is said to have published an anagram containing its composition in *De Mirabili Potestate Artis et Naturae* ('On the marvellous power of art and nature'). Unfortunately, no original copies of this work have survived, and the attribution rests largely on a repeat of the claim in *De Secretis Operibus Artis et Naturae et de Nullitae Magiae*, dated from 1248 to 1267, but now found only in seventeenth-century transcriptions.

The British Museum possesses a fifteenth-century copy of Bacon's *Opus Tertius* of 1268, though the accuracy of the popular transcription from Latin has often been questioned. It seems to give a crude but workable formula for gunpowder: seven parts saltpetre, five parts of hazel-twig charcoal, and five parts of sulphur.

There is no evidence that Bacon ever beat the path from incendiary compound to explosive, though he may have understood its potential. He was also aware that efficiency, and hence power, was linked with the purity of the ingredients, recommending that saltpetre (potassium nitrate) should be obtained by crystallisation from hot water. This was far better than traditional methods of scraping saltpetre from walls, or relying on urine-sodden aggregates of earth, animal droppings and wood-ash.

Gunpowder came from the East, though whether the Arabs or the Chinese should take credit is still vigorously contested. However, references in Chinese literature dating back to 1044 suggest that gunpowder was perfected towards the end of the Sung Dynasty (960-1279), and then travelled rapidly westward on Arab caravans to arrive in Europe in the middle of the thirteenth century.

Recognising the explosive properties of the new compound was only a short step from harnessing them for military purposes. The first known 'gun', which had appeared in Britain by 1322 or earlier, was a small narrow-mouthed iron pot loaded with an arrow. A cloth was wrapped around the shaft of the arrow to provide a rudimentary seal.

From such an uninspiring beginning, progress was rapid. Surprisingly large cannon were being used in war by the middle of the fourteenth century; the English are even said to have had four 'crayks of war' at the Battle of Crécy in 1346. The constituents of gunpowder had by this period become two-thirds saltpetre, two-ninths charcoal and one-ninth sulphur; roughly 67:22:11, very similar to the optimal 75:15:10. However, fourteenth-century powder was impure. Power was low, smoke was

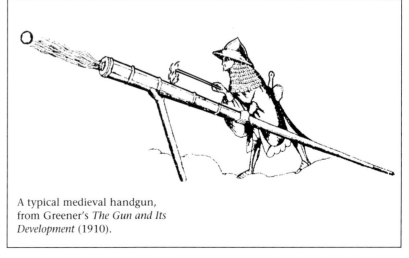

A typical medieval handgun, from Greener's *The Gun and Its Development* (1910).

6

excessive, and fouling was a hindrance.

Gunpowder customarily separated in transport, and had to be remixed before use. Spontaneous ignition could occur if this process was too robust, costing many a mixer his life until the introduction of 'corning' solved many of the problems. The mixture was wetted to a paste, forced through a sieve, and allowed to dry naturally. Propellant of this corned type had grains of surprisingly uniform size, which improved combustion, reduced fouling, and gave far greater power.

MEDIEVAL FIREARMS

The development of guns spread over several distinct phases. The earliest cannon not only grew rapidly in size but also became much more sophisticated. Carriages were added to help control the direction of the shot, and a rudimentary form of breech-loading was designed around a removable powder chamber and a sliding wedge. Unfortunately, poor metallurgy and erratic manufacture often made these early guns as much of a threat to the firers as the targets.

Gradually, however, smaller weapons appeared. The catalyst for this is widely believed to have been the introduction of multi-barrelled weapons called 'Ribaulds' or 'Ribauldequins', which consisted of a battery of individual barrels mounted on a sturdy wooden bed or a stout wheeled carriage. The barrels were generally parallel, though in a few cases they were splayed to broaden the field of fire.

These multi-barrel weapons clearly had advantages, but they were easily outflanked and taken from the rear. Barrels were eventually taken off the carriages, stocked, and issued to individual gunners. Each man could then select targets with far greater freedom than the ribauldequin.

These 'one-man' firearms were the first *handguns*, a term which originally referred to a weapon which was fired with both hands.

The butt of the stock, if fitted, was generally clamped beneath the upper arm, while a hook beneath the barrel of a 'Hakbutt' or 'Arquebuse' could be braced against a wall to reduce the effects of recoil. The oldest known weapons of this type dated from the middle of the fourteenth century, guns 'with tillers' (i.e., with butts) being inventoried in England as early as 1345.

Many of the first handguns were surprisingly small. The Tannenberg Gun, excavated in the nineteenth century from a castle in Germany which had been destroyed in 1399, has a .70 calibre barrel merely 12in long; it weighs only about 3lb without its long-lost stock.

Although some other guns surviving from this period are equally minuscule – a barrel from Mörkö in Sweden is just 7.6in long – several factors prevented them becoming typical. Among the limitations were the poor quality of medieval metallurgy, which could only be overcome by making components unnecessarily large or heavy. Bad-quality propellant was customarily accommodated by using heavy charges, but these occupied too much space in a short barrel to allow balls to be fired accurately.

THE WHEEL-LOCK

The size of firearms was not greatly changed by the introduction in the fifteenth century of match-lock ignition, which was eventually refined until the glowing slow match was pivoted into the priming pan by a mechanical linkage.

A major advance towards miniaturisation was made in Europe in the middle of the fifteenth century. Time had been told for years by ponderous weight-driven clocks, until the first spring-driven escapement appeared. Widely credited to Peter Henlein of Nuremberg but perhaps originating in France, this inspired the application of a similar mechanism to firearms, even though 200 years passed before clock springs were regarded as reliable enough for universal use.

The first wheel-lock is traditionally ascribed to Johann Kiefuss of Nuremberg, though the laurels are sometimes given to Leonardo da Vinci on the basis of *Codex Atlanticus* drawings of a tinder-lighter and a rudimentary wheel-type gunlock. Da Vinci's ideas have been transformed into three dimensions in the twentieth century and both have proved workable, but *Codex Atlanticus* is very difficult to date. Da Vinci clearly worked on his manuscript for many years, and may have been describing things that he had seen, rather than simply recording inventions of his own.

As the Italian polymath had also travelled widely in the first few years of the sixteenth century, the origins of the wheel-lock may still be justifiably sought in south Germany.

The *Codex Atlanticus* wheel-lock is now usually dated to about 1509, claims as early as 1482 being discredited. A similar proto-wheel-lock was drawn by Martin Löffelholz of Nuremberg in 1505, and a gun is known to have been constructed for the Bishop of Zagreb in 1507, even though the oldest survivor (by Bartholomäus Marquardt of Nuremberg) dates only from 1530.

A typical wheel-lock relied on a wedge of iron pyrites, which was held in the adjustable jaws of the cock against a serrated wheel. The spring was usually attached to the wheel spindle by a short chain, and was spanned ('wound') with a key which fitted over the wheel spindle. The spindle was turned until the trigger engaged the sear, or cock tail. When the trigger was pressed, the wheel was spun by the spring train and directed a shower of sparks into the pan containing the priming powder.

Ignition of this type was much more reliable than the match-lock, and guns would generally work in light rain as long as the priming powder and priming pan had been kept dry. Problems understandably lay in the brittleness of the earliest

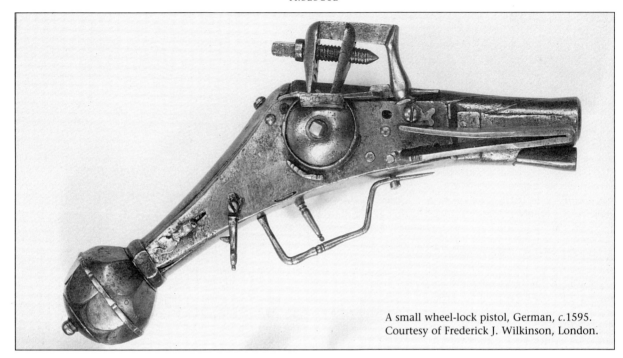

A small wheel-lock pistol, German, c.1595.
Courtesy of Frederick J. Wilkinson, London.

springs and in the soft pyrites, which would often disintegrate in the jaws of the cock, yet wheel-lock firearms were soon being made in large numbers.

This was partly due to the social standing of the clockmakers, who were among the most sophisticated craftsmen of their day. It was also assured by the patronage of the nobility, anxious to purchase the latest innovations, and by the blend of art and mechanics that distinguished so many individual items. As each clockmaker-gunsmith sought to attract patronage, guns became increasingly sophisticated. However, there was a limit to the dimensions of a handgun (even one designed to be fired from the shoulder), and thoughts turned instead to miniaturisation.

Wheel-lock pistols were soon reduced to such tiny proportions that they could be carried on a key chain, in a pouch, or concealed in the palm of the hand. These were usually miniatures instead of defensive weapons, even though almost all of them could shoot. Some would even have fired a bullet heavy enough to inflict an unpleasant short-range wound, but the guns were invariably regarded as noblemen's playthings and were thus a developmental cul-de-sac.

EVER-IMPROVING PERFORMANCE

Confining production to clockmaker-gunsmiths made wheel-locks very expensive, and they were never able to challenge the match-lock on the field of battle. The search for a cheaper alternative led to the snaphance lock (from the Dutch *snaphaan*, 'pecking chicken'), relying on a wedge of pyrites or a piece of flint clamped in the cock jaws. This scraped over a ribbed steel, pivoted on a spring to gain acceleration, which flew back and up when struck by the cock. The tail of the cock was caught internally by a laterally moving sear, to be released when the trigger lever was pressed.

The snaphance mechanism, easier to make than the wheel-lock, was soon being distributed widely in northern Europe. It was rivalled in southern Europe by the *miquelet* or Spanish lock, which combined pan and steel, omitted the tumbler, and carried the main spring externally.

The snaphance and miquelet were themselves supplanted in the seventeenth century by the flintlock, developed in France about 1612–15 by Marin le Bourgeoys (1550?–1638). The combination of the pan and the steel had been inspired by the miquelet, but changing the lateral sear for a vertical design allowed a 'half-cock' or safety notch to be added.

The greatest merit of the flintlock lay in simplicity. Though care was required to proportion the components correctly (this quickly became second nature to gun-lock makers), the delicacy of the smallest wheel-locks had been overcome. The flint was also much sturdier than pyrites had been.

The rapid spread of the flintlock was unquestionably promoted by military acceptance. It was soon being applied to almost every class of firearm, including even ships' cannon.

Pistols with flinted locks ranged from the largest military holster weapon to personal-protection guns no more than a few inches long. The story of the compact 'secret handgun', easily concealed in a pocket or purse, begins in this era.

SINGLE-SHOT PISTOLS

Acceptable reductions in size were still complicated by muzzle-loading and the poor thermal efficiency of gunpowder. Large charges were essential if enough power was to be generated, and the need of wadding to retain the ball wasted valuable bore length. Accuracy deteriorated as the barrel was shortened, and though this restriction was of no great importance for close-range defence, it undoubtedly restricted the utility of the smallest handguns. Excepting for miniatures, apprentice pieces, and an occasional gunsmith's sample, pistols with barrels of less than 3–4in were uncommon until the late eighteenth century.

The 'turn-off' barrel designs of the mid-seventeenth century were exceptions to this rule. These guns were loaded by detaching the barrel, which was screwed to the standing breech and had to be 'turned off'. Powder was then poured into the chamber in the standing breech, providing an accurately measured charge, the ball was inserted, and the barrel was replaced. The tight fit of the ball in the bore allowed turn-off pistols, which were sometimes also rifled, to shoot far more accurately than conventional muzzle-loaders. One story, possibly apocryphal, tells how Prince Rupert of the Rhine, the nephew of the English King Charles I, hit the weather vane on top of the spire of St Mary's Church in Oxford in 1646. The distance was probably 70–100 yards; very good shooting for a comparatively small pistol of this early date, and a tribute to the steadiness of Prince Rupert's hand.

Turn-off construction allowed some ultra-short-barrelled pistols to be made, and finally established the value of the pistol for personal defence. Unfortunately, largely owing to the poverty of seventeenth-century English metallurgy, the threads connecting the barrel and the breech were too easily damaged to allow turn-off barrel firearms to prosper. Pistols of this type were rapidly superseded by conventional muzzle-loaders, which lacked their rivals' good shooting qualities but were undeniably stronger.

The turn-off system enjoyed a lengthier period in vogue in the nineteenth century, when many

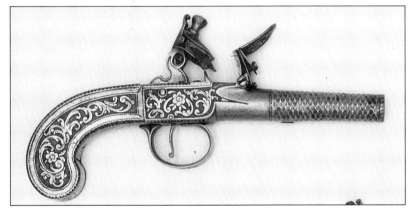

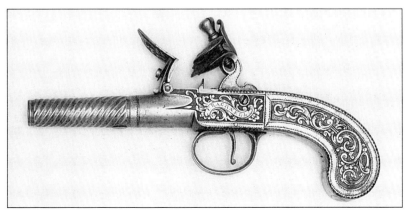

Left: a pair of small all-metal English flintlock pistols, elaborately decorated, marked by 'Cracknell'. It dates from the last quarter of the eighteenth century. Courtesy of Frederick J. Wilkinson, London.

9

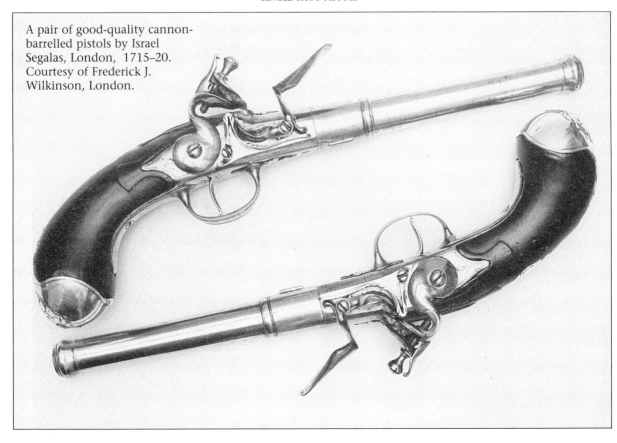

A pair of good-quality cannon-barrelled pistols by Israel Segalas, London, 1715–20. Courtesy of Frederick J. Wilkinson, London.

single-shot cap-lock pistols and a substantial number of pepper-boxes were made with detachable barrels.

Although short-barrel flintlock pistols were made throughout eighteenth-century Europe, Birmingham seems to have been the centre of production in this era. A contributory reason was the introduction of the *box-lock*. A gun of this type, fitted with a folding bayonet, was patented in England in March 1781 by John Waters (then trading in Snow Hill, Birmingham), who was active from 1765 until 1788. Packing the lockwork into a self-contained casing was much better than letting a conventional side-lock into a wooden stock. A separate butt could be attached with straps, or simply by inserting the tip of the butt into the lockwork case. The barrels, often swamped or bell-mouthed (even if parallel-bored), could be forged integrally with the lockwork case to gain appreciably in strength.

THE EARLIEST 'SECRET FIREARMS'

Many guns of this type were made in the eighteenth century, though not all could be categorised as handguns. Alarm and trap guns often assumed prodigious proportions; so, too, did guns combined with polearms, even though their barrels may have been quite short. Many gunsmiths made small flintlock pistols, and others were created by apprentices keen to advertise their newly-acquired skills. Greater dexterity was needed to make tiny weapons than large ones, in which the fit of the parts and the delicacy of decoration presented much less of a challenge.

A typical pistol of the 1750s, one of a pair, was made by William Sharpe of Hayden Yard, Minories, London. The son of a gunsmith of the same name, Sharpe was admitted as a Freeman of the Gunmakers Company in 1734 and remained active into the 1760s. His gun is 6.7in long and has a 2.25in barrel with a bore of about .43in. The cylindrical brass barrel is forged integrally with the box-lock, which is engraved with a trophy of arms and the maker's name. A slab-sided walnut butt attaches to straps running backward from the rear of the lock casing, and the cock has a ring throat.

Small enough to be carried in a gentleman's pocket or a lady's muffler, guns of this type undoubtedly featured in many a lurid crime in an era renowned for lawlessness. Footpads, cutpurses and highwaymen threatened the unwary traveller, and smugglers and wreckers followed their traditional calling along many a coastline.

Larger guns, short-barrelled but too big for a pocket, could be concealed in everyday objects. Books were a particular favourite, pages being hollowed to hold the gun or, alternatively, a special insert could be prepared. And the category of secret handguns could perhaps include the cheat's 'smooth-bore' duelling pistols. These had shallow rifling which stopped far enough from the muzzle to be seen only by an unusually suspicious Second.

PERCUSSION IGNITION

The success of the flinted locks allowed firearms to spread throughout the world, even though ignition of this type was still far from ideal. A delay could be sensed between pressing the trigger, the ignition of the priming, and the firing of the main charge to propel a ball along the barrel and out of the muzzle towards the target. This 'waiting time' was of little regard on the battlefield until sharpshooters armed with the first military rifles were asked to engage individual targets, but it was of great concern to sportsmen and wildfowlers, as the flash of the priming gave a canny game bird just enough time to change course before the main charge fired.

The solution to the problem was found by a Presbyterian minister, Alexander Forsyth of the parish of Belhelvie in Aberdeenshire. Metallic fulminates had been known for only a few years when Forsyth made his first unsuccessful attempts to ignite them with a modified flinted lock, but not until 1805 did he realise that the key to progress lay in striking mercuric fulminate in a confined space.

The story of official disparagement is well known – the Master-General of the Ordnance eventually ejected the inventor and 'his rubbish' from the Tower of London – but the assistance of the engineer James Watt allowed Forsyth to perfect his 'scent-bottle' lock. The sobriquet arose from its resemblance to the cosmetic phials of the day. Forsyth was granted English Patent 3032 in April 1807, protecting his design until 1821. The first guns were made by John Prosser of Charing Cross, London, but were so unsatisfactory that the Forsyth Patent Gun Company began work on its own account in 1809. Pistols, rifles and shotguns were made for some years in a workshop at No. 10 Piccadilly.

The original Forsyth lock was basically a rotary priming-powder magazine mounted on the outside of a conventional lock plate, in front of a hammer with a flat face. Once the gun had been loaded from the muzzle, the hammer was thumbed back to half cock, and the priming magazine was rotated through 180°. This allowed a tiny amount of mercuric fulminate, called 'oxymuriate salts' by Forsyth, to enter the flash-hole channel. The magazine was then returned to its initial position to isolate its contents from the flash hole. The hammer could be withdrawn to full cock, the trigger was pressed, and the main spring drove the hammer forward on to a spring-loaded pin protruding from the top of the magazine casing. This pin was driven down into the flash-hole aperture to detonate the fulminate, and the flash from the fulminate then ignited the main charge.

Even the earliest Forsyth scent-bottle locks were waterproof, and greatly improved ignition compared with flinted locks. However, complexity made them expensive, and the spectre of premature ignition was raised by the effects of wear on the magazine spindle. The mechanism had to be cleaned regularly and the priming salts were notably corrosive.

THE PERCUSSION CAP

Drawbacks both real and imaginary limited the success of the scent-bottle lock. It had been fitted to a few handguns, including a pocket pistol or two, but its greatest legacy was to persuade gunmakers that fulminate ignition was preferable to flint sparks. Long before Forsyth died in 1843, many men had attempted to improve on his basic idea. Some of their proposals were ludicrous and others were dangerous, but a few worked well enough to foretell the future.

Forsyth himself proposed a drum of priming powder, rotating

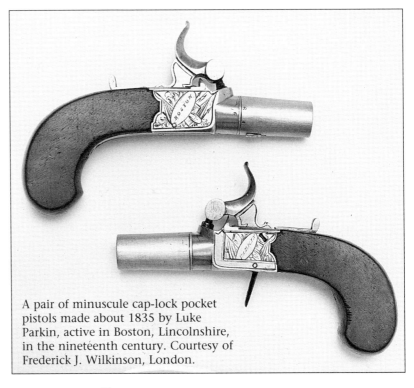

A pair of minuscule cap-lock pocket pistols made about 1835 by Luke Parkin, active in Boston, Lincolnshire, in the nineteenth century. Courtesy of Frederick J. Wilkinson, London.

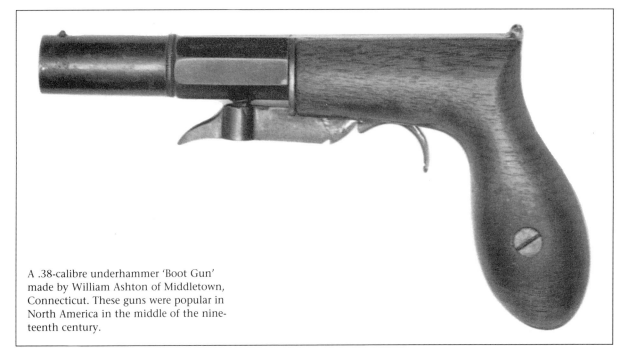

A .38-calibre underhammer 'Boot Gun' made by William Ashton of Middletown, Connecticut. These guns were popular in North America in the middle of the nineteenth century.

on a vertical axis, while Joseph Manton, then among London's leading gunmakers, patented the insertion of a pellet or 'pill' inside a hollow-face hammer in 1816. Across the Atlantic, American Samuel Guthrie suggested partially inserting a tube of primer in the flash hole so that the protruding portion could be struck by the descending hammer.

Several disc-primer systems were developed, not unlike the present-day children's cap guns. Christian Sharps and Butterfield & Marshall both developed satisfactory single-cap systems, whereas Edward Maynard, basing his ideas on work undertaken in France in the 1820s, proffered a continuous paper roll.

Most of the ideas which reached production were better than Forsyth's scent-bottle, though some had disadvantages of their own. Pill primers were especially vulnerable to knocks and blows, priming tubes could fly out of flash-holes on ignition, and discs or tape were vulnerable to moisture.

The answer was ultimately found in the percussion cap, containing mercuric fulminate or potassium chlorate in a copper 'hat' sealed with a tin-foil disc and shellac. Caps were virtually impervious to water and, once the manufacturing process had been perfected, could be made surprisingly cheaply. Many inventors claimed to have developed the first cap. They included Peter Hawker, the famed sportsman; Joseph Egg and James Purdey, leading London gunsmiths of the day; and Edward Goode Wright, whose ideas were published in 1823 in *The Philosophical Magazine and Journal*. The earliest traceable patent was granted in France in July 1820 to an incorrigible copyist named Prélat, and is unlikely to have been original.

First among many claimants is Joshua Shaw, who is believed to have made an iron-sheet cap in 1814, followed by pewter and then copper versions by 1816. Shaw emigrated in 1817 from England to the USA, where a patent was eventually granted in June 1822. Shaw subsequently stated that he had doubted whether his cap could have been registered in England owing to the existence of Forsyth's patent (which ran until 1821), and ascribed the delay in the American grant to the two-year residential qualification necessary before the application could be filed. The destruction by fire of the US Patent Office in 1836 may have removed evidence which could have supported Shaw's claim.

Whatever its genesis may have been, the percussion cap was soon established as the only reliable method of igniting the gunpowder charge in firearms. Although construction of the earliest guns often differed considerably in detail (especially flintlock conversions), the pattern eventually settled on a side- or back-action lock. A flat-faced hammer struck a copper cap placed over a nipple, relying on a central flash hole to transmit the priming flash to the main charge. Caps and nipples were made in differing sizes; handguns did not need the large musket-type caps owing to the restricted size of their gunpowder charges.

The advent of the cap-lock gave the development of secret firearms a great boost, largely because of more reliable ignition. Flinted locks were not suited to guns which were carried loose in the pocket, as the fine-grain priming

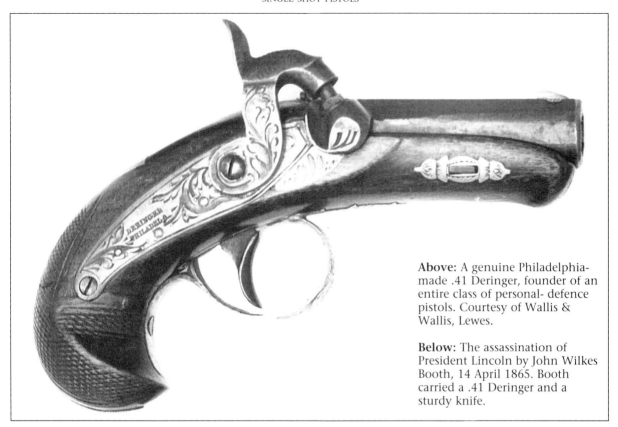

Above: A genuine Philadelphia-made .41 Deringer, founder of an entire class of personal-defence pistols. Courtesy of Wallis & Wallis, Lewes.

Below: The assassination of President Lincoln by John Wilkes Booth, 14 April 1865. Booth carried a .41 Deringer and a sturdy knife.

powder could leak from the pan if the steel was a poor fit. Although it was risky to carry a capped pistol in such circumstances, especially with the hammer down, preparing to fire a pre-loaded cap-lock was much simpler than a flintlock.

Most cap-lock 'secret handguns', at least until the introduction of the pepperbox and the revolver, were essentially similar to their flintlock precursors. This was partly due to reliance on muzzle loading and, as often as not, a single barrel.

The crudest short-barrel cap-lock pistols were made by the thousand in Birmingham and Liége, often distinguished only by their proof marks (though construction may also suggest origins). They were so cheap that they appealed to virtually every class of society.

A typical Belgian-made box lock gun of the 1840s, with a calibre of about .41in, had a three-inch brass barrel forged integrally with a lock-case; the hammer and the nipple were mounted centrally, typical of guns of this type. The barrel was octagonal for virtually all its length, excepting the belled mouth, and had a short spring-loaded folding bayonet on the right side of the muzzle. The finely chequered walnut butt lacked a butt-cap, which was also typical of the cheapest products.

Guns of this general pattern were often known as 'Travelling Pistols' or 'Coach Pistols', owing to the defence they supposedly offered travellers against brigands, highwaymen and footpads. Some guns were small, while others approached the size of duelling pistols. Quality varied from exceptionally fine to horrible, a range reflected in the price structure. The best guns were made in matched pairs, or a brace of pairs of differing sizes contained, with matching accessories, in satin- or baize-lined cases. Some had folding triggers which sprang down out of the frame when the hammer was cocked, while others had captive rammers on swivels beneath the barrel.

THE CAP-LOCK DERINGERS

The cap-lock revolvers offered by Samuel Colt and his rivals in the middle of the nineteenth century clearly held great advantages over any single-shot pistol. However, not only were revolvers expensive, but production was initially too small to dominate the market. The single-barrel pistol was easier to make, co-existing with more sophisticated rivals until the American Civil War.

The cap-locks made in Philadelphia from the 1840s onward by Henry Deringer were the most popular. Deringer's holster pistols had attained a certain amount of success in the Texarkana in the 1840s, but the guns with which his name is now associated could be hidden in a pocket or a hand. They were generally .41-calibre back-action cap-locks with rifled barrels as short as two inches, reducing overall length to just 4½in. Genuine Philadelphia-made Deringers were marked H. DERINGER over PHILADELA. or PHILA. on the lock. The barrel key was customarily retained by a pineapple-finial plate, barrels displayed a false damascus twist, and the locks were invariably case-hardened. The metalwork was usually blued, though nickel- and silver-plated trigger guards and barrel-wedge plates could be supplied to order.

The lasting success of the Deringer was due to the Gold Rush of 1849, which turned California from its Spanish colonial slumber into a rampaging boom economy. Limitations on Deringer's production capacity, which was too small to satisfy all but a fraction of the demand, persuaded many gunsmiths to copy the Philadelphia-made pocket pistol. Among the legions of copyists were Slotter & Company and A. J. Plate of San Francisco. Some guns were even given spurious authenticity by the marks of Philadelphia tailor Jacob Deringer, who granted appropriate 'licences' to several gunsmiths. The .38-calibre derringers made by Jesse Butterfield of

Philadelphia usually had a patented priming tube mounted vertically ahead of the hammer, where it could feed a pellet over the nipple each time the mechanism was cocked. Ingenuity of this type, however, was the exception to the simple-copy rule.

After the death of Henry Deringer in 1867, his executors pursued many infringers through the Federal courts, but enforcement of the decisions was often impossible in areas which had not even been admitted to the Union. Transgressors simply continued to make their derringers until cartridge pistols appeared in quantity.

The Deringer was the ideal covert weapon in such an environment, acting as a back-up for larger guns. The .41-calibre ball was effective at close range, provided enough powder was used, and the tiny pistol could be tucked in a gambler's boot or a bordello girl's garter. Among the Westerners known to have carried derringers was William F. 'Buffalo Bill' Cody, who acquired a pair of genuine Philadelphia-made guns in 1865, but the most notorious of all incidents involving cap-lock derringers took place in Washington, D.C., in the evening of Friday 14 April 1865. President Abraham Lincoln was enjoying a performance of 'Tom Taylor's Celebrated Eccentric Comedy *Our American Cousin*' in Ford's Theatre on Tenth Street above East, 'for the Benefit and Last Night of Miss Laura Keene, the Distinguished Manageress, Authoress and Actress'. Unnoticed during the performance, John Wilkes Booth crept into Lincoln's box, drew a battered Philadelphia Deringer and fired a .41 ball into the back of the President's head to avenge the defeat of the Confederacy. Booth escaped in the confusion but did not get far. Hindered by a broken foot bone and a $100,000 price on his head, he was hunted down and killed near Bowling Green, Virginia, twelve days later. Lincoln, grievously wounded, was carried to a house across the street from the theatre, but died early in the morning of 15 April.

Excepting the Deringer and its facsimiles, single-barrel cap-lock pocket pistols were uncommon in North America. The smallest of the several Lindsay Young America guns was broadly comparable, though its barrel contained two superimposed charges. These were fired separately by two individual hammers; however, unless the charges were separated by properly greased wads, ignition of the first (front) charge was apt to fire the second (rear) charge at the same time.

METALLIC-CARTRIDGE DERRINGERS

The cap-lock pocket pistols were slowly superseded by cartridge patterns in the 1860s. Patented in February 1861 by Daniel Moore, the .41 rimfire National Model No. 1 pistol was made in quantity by Moore's Patent Fire Arms Company and the National Arms Company of Brooklyn. This brass-framed derringer had a sheath trigger and a barrel which pivoted laterally to expose the breech. The No. 1 was undeniably

clumsy, but it was strong enough to be used as a knuckleduster.

Production of the Moore derringers began before the patent had been granted; the first guns, therefore, lack the patent-date markings. Later examples had different hammers and a better breech catch; some guns had extractors, but others did not. The National Model No. 2 was similar to the No. 1, except that the gap between the trigger and the grip was increased. Grip-plates of walnut or rosewood were fitted.

The National Arms Company was acquired by Colt in 1870, production of the No. 1 and No. 2 derringers shifting from Brooklyn to the Colt factory in Hartford, Connecticut. Only the manufacturer's marks were changed. Colt is said to have made about 15,000 Moore-type derringers, many of which were sold as matched pairs. Hand-cut scroll engraving was common.

The No. 3 Colt derringer, designed by Alexander Thuer in the early 1870s, had a barrel which pivoted sideways to load. Spent cases were ejected automatically as the breech opened. Most of the 45,000 guns made by 1912

fired .41 centre-fire ammunition, though a few alternative chamberings were supplied to special order; 2½in barrels were standard. Finished in plain blue or nickel plate, the No. 3 had bird's head grips of walnut, rosewood, or mother-of-pearl. The earliest guns had a bolster on the frame beneath the barrel, but later examples have straight frames. The radius of the grip and the shape of the hammer-spur were also changed.

Thuer-type derringers were very popular with copyists. The 'O.K.' and Victor pistols made by Marlin were essentially similar, as were XL patterns made by Hopkins & Allen and their successors, Forehand & Wadsworth, until 1889.

Some American 'Cartridge Derringer' Manufacturers
Bacon Arms Company, Norwich, Connecticut
Ballard & Fairbanks, Worcester, Massachusetts
Brown Manufacturing Company, Newburyport, Massachusetts
Made the Southerner Derringer (1869–73).
Colt's Patent Fire Arms Manufacturing Company, Hartford, Connecticut

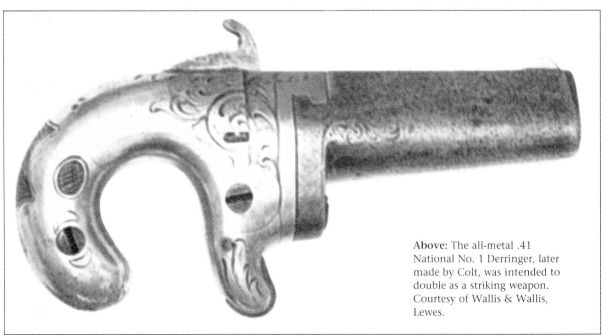

Above: The all-metal .41 National No. 1 Derringer, later made by Colt, was intended to double as a striking weapon. Courtesy of Wallis & Wallis, Lewes.

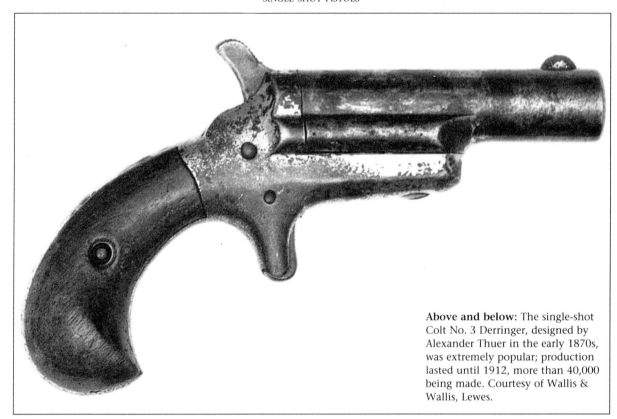

Above and below: The single-shot Colt No. 3 Derringer, designed by Alexander Thuer in the early 1870s, was extremely popular; production lasted until 1912, more than 40,000 being made. Courtesy of Wallis & Wallis, Lewes.

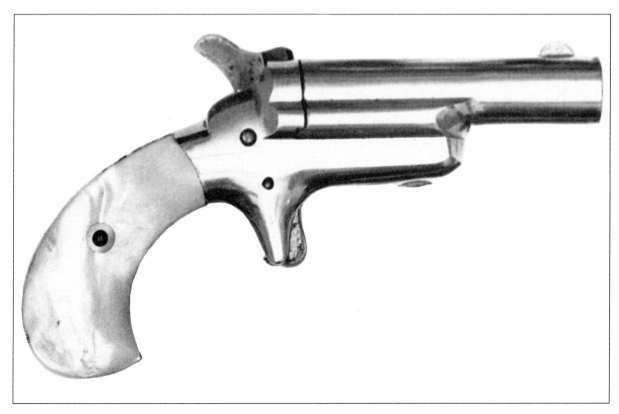

No. 1 and No. 2 were identical with the National patterns.

Connecticut Arms Company, Glastonbury, Connecticut

Made the Bulldog or Bulldozer, patented by Henry Hammond.

Forehand & Wadsworth, Worcester, Massachusetts

Hopkins & Allen, Norwich, Connecticut

Made the 'XL' series.

John Marlin, New Haven, Connecticut

Made the 'O.K.' and the Victor.

Merrimack Arms & Manufacturing Company, Newburyport, Massachusetts

Made the Southerner Derringer (1867–9).

Moore's Patent Fire Arms Company, Brooklyn, New York

Morgan & Clapp, New Haven, Connecticut

National Arms Company, Brooklyn, New York

Remington Arms Company, Ilion, New York State

Made the Deringer Pistol, patented by William Elliot, and the rolling-block type Vest Pocket Pistol.

J. Stevens Arms Company, Chicopee Falls, Massachusetts

Made the Vest Pocket or 'Kick-Up', the Gem, and a series of proprietary designs.

THE LIBERATOR PISTOL

The cartridge pistol lost much of its popularity to the revolver in the 1870s, particularly small pinfires in Europe and the 'Suicide Specials' in North America. The single-shot designs made in the twentieth century have almost exclusively been restricted to game-hunting or target shooting.

One noteworthy exception was the Liberator pistol, developed on behalf of the US Joint Psychological Warfare Committee by a team led by George Hyde and made by the Inland Division of General Motors. Hyde is best known for his submachine-guns.

Known officially as the 'Flare Projector, Caliber .45' (FP-45) to disguise their true purpose, Liber-

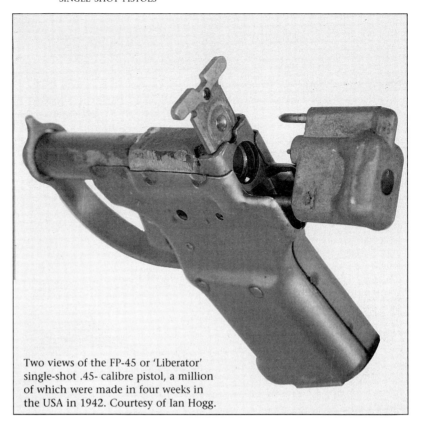

Two views of the FP-45 or 'Liberator' single-shot .45-calibre pistol, a million of which were made in four weeks in the USA in 1942. Courtesy of Ian Hogg.

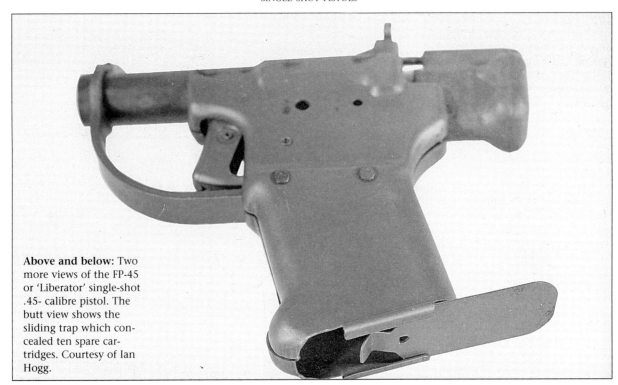

Above and below: Two more views of the FP-45 or 'Liberator' single-shot .45- calibre pistol. The butt view shows the sliding trap which concealed ten spare cartridges. Courtesy of Ian Hogg.

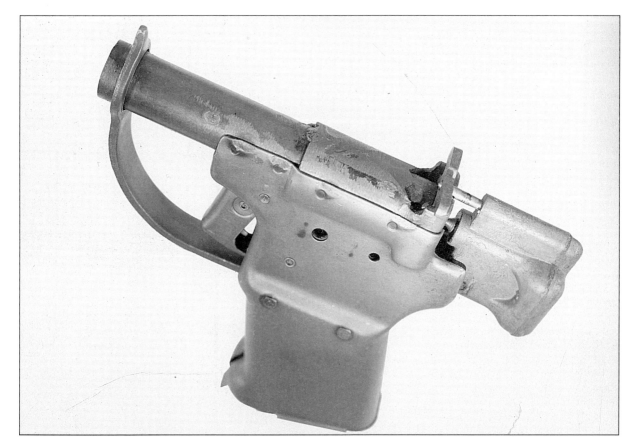

ators were to be dropped behind German lines to arm partisans and resistance personnel. A million of them were ordered in May 1942 and delivered four weeks later by the Guide Lamp Division factory in Anderson, Indiana, at a total cost of $1,710,000. They were easy to conceal, being merely 5½in long with 4¼in smoothbore barrels and a weight of 21½oz.

The design was extremely simple, relying on stampings and spot-welding; several of the parts fulfilled more than one function. Accompanied by a diagrammatic instruction sheet, each Liberator was packed in a waxed waterproof carton with ten .45 ACP cartridges hidden inside the hollow butt. The gun was operated by pulling the locking block back and turning it to the left through 90°. This cocked the striker and allowed the breech-plate to be slid vertically to open the chamber. A spent case could be punched out with a separate ejector rod (a stout twig could often suffice), allowing a new round to be pushed into the chamber. The breech-plate was closed, the locking block was returned, and the Liberator could be fired.

About 500,000 guns were shipped to Britain, the remainder going to China and the Pacific. Few were ever used; the Far Eastern theatres were sceptical of the crudity of the single-shot Liberator and its very poor accuracy. The story in Europe was no better. Production of Sten Guns in Britain had accelerated to such a level that the authorities sensibly decided that a 9mm submachine- gun, particularly one which shared a standard German service cartridge, was much more useful than a crude pistol which would be useless once its ten .45in rounds had been expended. Most of the Liberators were therefore dumped in the Irish Sea or simply melted down to allow their valuable steel content to be recycled.

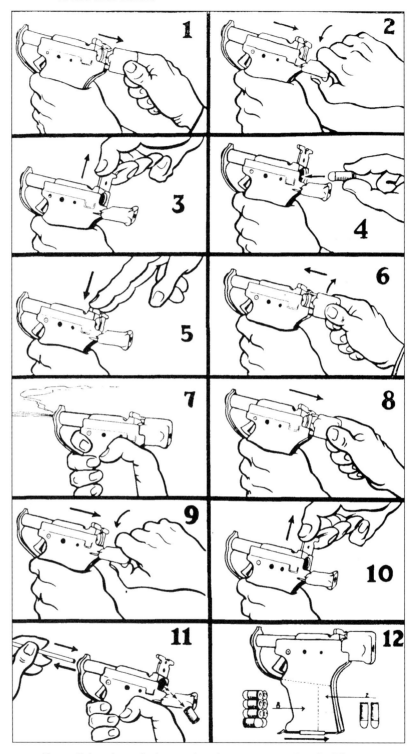

Above: Taken from the instruction sheet accompanying the Liberator, these twelve drawings show how the gun was to be used. The operations are self-explanatory.

COMBINATION WEAPONS

The practice of combining firearms with other weapons has been very popular throughout history, largely owing to unreliability and the one-shot nature of most of the guns made before 1850. Match-locks were the first to be combined, with a mace or battleaxe, but the most forbidding of these weapons was the Holy Water Sprinkler. The name apparently comes not from the *aspergillum*, a container used in religious services, but instead from medieval slang: to 'sprinkle Holy Water' simply meant to 'spill blood'.

Classifiable as one-hand weapons by stretching the imagination, fifteenth-century Holy Water Sprinklers had two, three, four or even six gun barrels on a common haft. The barrels were invariably retained by iron collars set with prominent spikes. Although wheel-lock Holy Water Sprinklers survive from the sixteenth century, the match-locks were simpler and more durable.

Cap-lock combination weapons are scarcer than their flintlock predecessors, largely owing to the emergence of multi-shot firearms only a few years after the perfection of the percussion cap. The Elgin Cutlass Pistols can be discounted, partly because they were developed for a specific purpose

but also because they were so large. No attempt was made to hide the gun portion of these weapons from view, but the same cannot always be said of pistol-knives.

SWORD-PISTOLS
Weapons of this type remained in vogue into the present century. The construction of many shows that they were not made with the primary intention of keeping the presence of a firearm secret, but simply provided another means of defence in one unit. The pistol component is usually easy to detect; the direction of fire is customarily towards the blade tip. Less obvious are the guns

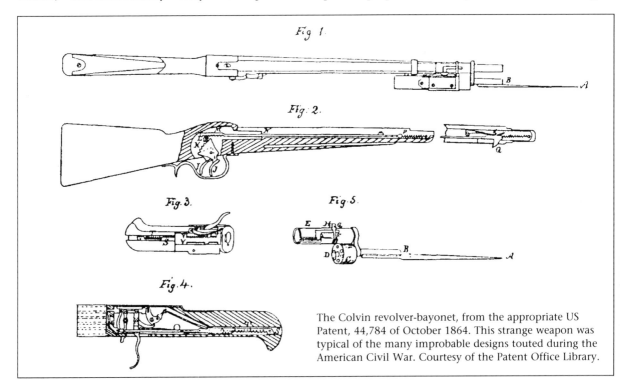

The Colvin revolver-bayonet, from the appropriate US Patent, 44,784 of October 1864. This strange weapon was typical of the many improbable designs touted during the American Civil War. Courtesy of the Patent Office Library.

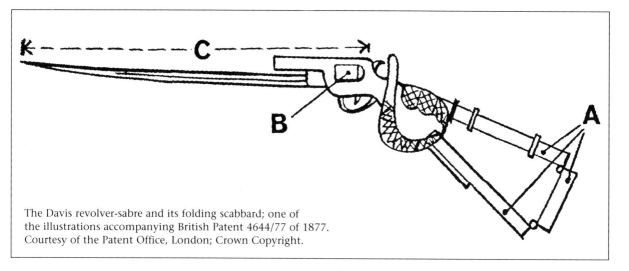

The Davis revolver-sabre and its folding scabbard; one of
the illustrations accompanying British Patent 4644/77 of 1877.
Courtesy of the Patent Office, London; Crown Copyright.

in which the pistol barrel forms the hilt. Many of these are designed to fire backwards, away from the blade tip; triggers were often hidden, and even the presence of the cock and frizzen may not be obvious at a casual glance. Cap-locks of this type were even easier to disguise than the flintlocks, particularly if enclosed locks and bar hammers were fitted.

With one or two exceptions, where the gun, usually single-shot, was concealed in the hilt and fired backwards, combinations of pistols and swords were rarely secretive. Most of those made during the second half of the nineteenth century incorporated revolvers, and the bulky cylinders could hardly be hidden. Typical of these was the revolver-sabre patented in the USA in March 1862 by Robert Colvin of Lancaster, Pennsylvania.

Originating during the Civil War, just one of many strange weapons being promoted enthusiastically across the USA, the Colvin sabre-revolver at least made the transition from patent-specifica- tion drawing to hardware. Unfortunately the manufacturer has never been satisfactorily identified, though there were many in the Lancaster area, the original home of the American or Pennsylvanian Long Rifle, who could have been responsible. The `gun part' of the weapon was a five-shot cap-lock revolver rotated by a double-acting trigger within the crossguard of the sword.

Another burst of enthusiasm occurred in Britain, owing to an increase in colonial campaigns. A patent protecting a cap-lock revolver-sabre was granted in 1864 to Isaiah Williams, acting for an Italian designer named Micheloni. As late as December 1877, Walter Davis of 'Parkrange', Westbury Park, Durdham Down, Bristol, was granted protection for a combina- tion weapon similar to Colvin's revolver-sabre. Additional novelty lay in the sectional construction of the scabbard, which could be fold- ed to act as a shoulder stock. A broadly comparable patent for a revolver-sword was subsequently granted to R. Howard of Southampton in 1882.

KNIFE-PISTOLS

Note: bladed cane- and knuckle- duster-pistols are considered in the relevant sections.

Most knife-pistols are anonymous, which is particularly unfortunate if it obscures the origins of design. One German-made piece, for example, has a short barrel and a combination hammer-bar/breech block released by a small folding lever beneath the grip. Another interesting example – completely unmarked – has two barrels, each flanking a central two-edged dag- ger and fired by a laterally-moving hammer forming the crossguard. Proof marks may occasionally identify nationality, but many pis- tol-knives pre-date the establish-

Below: This flintlock knife pistol typifies the combination weapons made in the eighteenth century. Courtesy of Frederick J. Wilkinson.

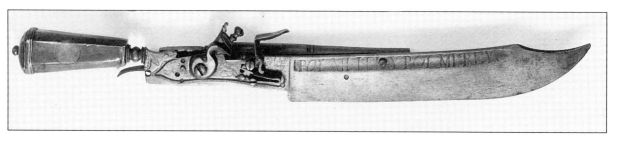

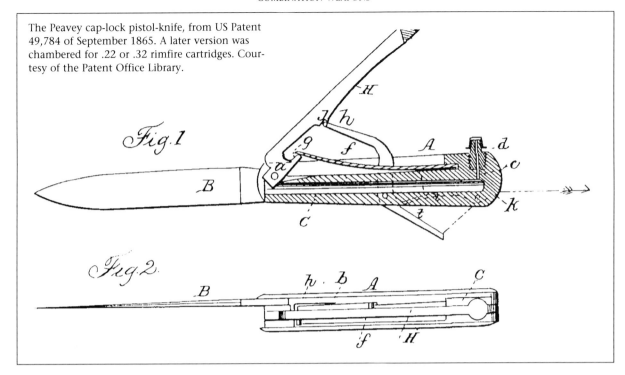

The Peavey cap-lock pistol-knife, from US Patent 49,784 of September 1865. A later version was chambered for .22 or .32 rimfire cartridges. Courtesy of the Patent Office Library.

Fig.1

Fig.2

ment of mandatory proof. This is notably true of pre-1891 German examples, as well as those made in the USA (where there is still no national proof system).

Birmingham gunmaker John Waters patented a pistol with a spring-loaded bayonet as long ago as 1781. Although the blade was mounted on the right side of the muzzle, where it was scarcely secret, Waters' ideas soon inspired copies, near-copies and improved designs. Some of the vaunted improvements were nothing more than blades hidden between barrels or in the fore-ends where a rammer was often carried, but others were much more interesting.

The Cutlass Pistol designed by George Elgin was originally conceived to accompany the US South Seas Expedition of 1837, but was not successful. Indeed, there is doubt whether any actually went to the South Seas. A few smaller examples were subsequently offered commercially, but did not sell well. The principal promoters then withdrew in disarray.

Many attempts were made to provide multi-shot combination weapons in this particular class. Colt made a double-action Paterson-type revolver with a sturdy blade beneath the muzzle, and substantial quantities of pinfire examples were made in Europe in a range of sizes. Most of the pinfires will prove to have been made in Liége, but Spanish-made examples are known and a few were doubtless made in Birmingham.

The disguises adopted by knife-pistols were usually much better than those of the bladed revolvers. The best known of these lesser weapons were made by Unwin & Rodgers of Sheffield, apparently beginning in the 1850s. Later examples (possibly made after 1867) were marked by Joseph Rodgers or, from about 1888 onward, Joseph Rodgers & Sons. These companies all used a distinctive trademark in the form of a six-point linear star and a cross patée. Joseph Rodgers also sometimes simply used ACME, METEOR, STAR AND CROSS, the German-language version STERNENKREUZ, the misleading U☆S, or '6 Norfolk Street, Sheffield' instead of his name.

The earliest examples were single-barrel cap-locks with two folding knife blades beneath the handgrip. Some grips were wood, others were staghorn and a few were chequered gutta-percha. The barrel of these pistol-knives lay along the top of the grip, where it was clearly visible, and the trigger folded up beneath the grip to prevent snagging inside a pocket. Cap-lock models often carried a small scissors-type ball mould and a rammer in the slots in the grip, where they were held by friction. Most guns, cap-lock and metal-case cartridge alike, had a small hinged-lid trap in the butt to carry bullets or spare .22 Short cartridges.

Unwin & Rodgers also made a few twin-barrel pistol-knives, marked SELF PROTECTOR, with as many as four blades. These generally had twin triggers. A few guns had a distinctive false breech which had to be lifted before the extractor could be activated.

Among the most heavily disguised of all pistol-knives were the pen- or clasp-knife patterns, which give few clues to their additional functions. Andrew Peavey of South Montville, Maine, patented a cap-lock version in September 1865 and a rimfire adaptation in March 1866. The Peavey pistol-knife had a single folding blade, offset to one side to allow a barrel to run the length of the grip beneath the elongated hammer bar. The gun was fired by pulling up on the rear of the hammer against the pressure of the leaf spring, until it was held by a serpentine catch doubling as the trigger lever. Pressing the tail of the catch released the hammer, which flew shut to strike either a cap on the nipple or the rim of a cartridge.

The Bazar clasp knife-pistol was made in Germany before the First World War, apparently on the basis of 'Springer'-brand collar-lock knife parts purchased from Wilhelm Weltersbach of Solingen (though there is no evidence that Weltersbach combined the components into weapons). The pivoting barrel-block usually held a single .22 Short rimfire cartridge, and the spring-loaded striker was controlled by a small button trigger. Intended for sporting use, these guns may have staghorn, mother-of-pearl, wooden, or chequered rubber grips. They also often have auxiliary extractors for shotgun cartridges, marked C-12 or C-16 depending on gauge.

The knife-pistol patented in the USA in February 1916 by Leo Rogers was basically a penknife divided longitudinally into two compartments. One contained a brace of folding blades; the other held the striker, its spring, the trigger mechanism and a minuscule barrel containing a single .22 Short rimfire cartridge fired by a latch in the right grip. The barrel-block could be pivoted to load or eject.

Penknife guns were surprisingly popular. The Defender and the Huntsman, 3in and 4in long respectively, were made in the early 1920s by the American Novelty Company of Chicago. They were similar to the Rogers patterns described above, but relied on a radial firing lever set into the upper strap of the grip instead of a pivoting trigger latch. An advert placed in *Popular Science Monthly* in 1923, showing one of these guns being used to protect a child from a mad dog, claimed that it was a 'practical pocket firearm! Easy to carry, absolutely safe, and has a thousand uses. Not a toy, but a sturdy well-made combination knife and pistol of finely tempered steel. Shoots regular .22 cal. cartridges – hard and straight . . . American made and guaranteed.'

These straight-grip pen- and clasp-knife pistols were very easily disguised but difficult to hold and aim. In these respects they were inferior to the pistol-grip patterns. Typical of the latter was the 'Little Pal', made by the L. G. Polhemus Manufacturing Company of Miami in Arizona. It was apparently offered in differing forms, as one gun is marked MOD. 23 – 22 SHORTS ONLY, while another reportedly chambers .25 ACP. The Little Pal was basically a bolt-action pistol with additional knife blades beneath the muzzle. The guns generally had simulated bone or staghorn fore-ends and chequered plastic grips displaying an encircled 'S' mark.

Knife pistols were customarily single-shot, which enabled them to be kept as compact as possible. However, a few double-barrel examples survive and a few European guns (generally Belgian) incorporate small-calibre pinfire revolvers. These usually date from 1870–1914.

KNUCKLEDUSTER PISTOLS
The idea of combining a handgun with a means of striking an opponent is very old. It was particularly important in the earliest days of firearms history, when the guns were customarily single-shot and always likely to misfire. Combinations of pistols with maces or ball butts were tried in small numbers (the latter are said to have been particularly popular in the Caucasus mountains), and some small

pocketable all-metal guns were made in the eighteenth and nineteenth centuries.

The most popular form of striking weapon was based on the knuckleduster, an aid known since the days of the Roman gladiatorial arenas, though the name did not enter English (by way of American slang) until the middle of the nineteenth century.

William and John Rigby of Dublin made a large number of multi-barrel cap-locks with an all-metal grip and a rotating striker plate on the nose of the hammer. Four-barrel guns are most common, often made in matched pairs, though three- and six-barrel variants are said to have been made. They were specifically designed to serve as striking weapons after all the shots had been fired, and have a distinctive finger-hole through the grip. Reloading was accomplished by unscrewing the barrels.

The single-shot cartridge derringers made by Moore's Patent Fire Arms Company, the National Arms Company, and then Colt's Patent Firearms Mfg Co. were conceived as dual-purpose shooting/striking weapons. They are described in the section devoted to cartridge derringers.

A more efficient knuckleduster-pistol was patented in the USA in December 1865 by James Reid of Catskill in New York State. Marketed under the brandname 'My Friend', Reid's design was basically a solid-frame barrelless revolver with an all-metal frame extended to contain a ring-grip for the smallest or fourth finger of the firer's hand. The gun also had a sliding safety catch beneath the frame which could lock the cylinder when the hammer was midway between chambers. Consequently, My Friends always had an odd number of chambers (usually five). Reloading was simply a matter of releasing the axis pin and removing the cylinder. About 20,000 Reid revolvers were made from 1866 until 1880, when they were superseded by a variant with a short bar-

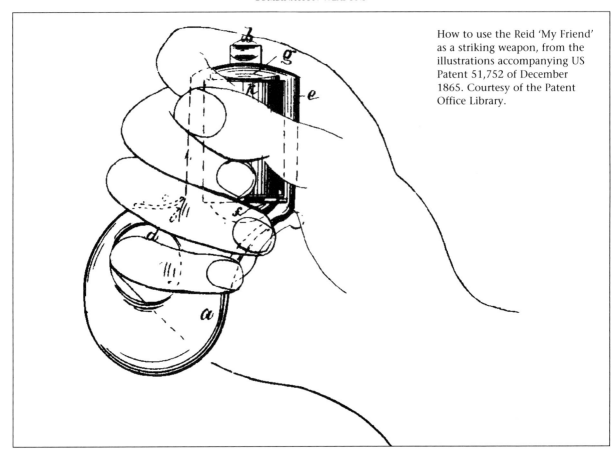

How to use the Reid 'My Friend' as a striking weapon, from the illustrations accompanying US Patent 51,752 of December 1865. Courtesy of the Patent Office Library.

rel. Marked REID'S NEW MODEL MY FRIEND, this lasted until 1884. It is not known whether the changes were made to improve accuracy or to reduce accidents arising from the absence of a barrel on the original gun.

Seven-shot .22, five-shot .32 and five-shot .41 versions of My Friend are known, usually chambered for rimfire ammunition. The distinctive safety catches were fitted to some (but by no means all) of the .22 and .32 guns, but invariably appear on the uncommon .41. Fewer than 500 of these large-calibre rimfires were made.

The European equivalent of Reid's knuckleduster revolver was the 'Apache', credited to the Belgian gunmaker Louis Dolne, trading in the 1870s from Rue Janfosse in Liége. Named after the Parisian street gangs of the period, the barrelless pinfire revolver had a spurless hammer, a folding trigger, a swivelling knife blade on the lower edge of the frame and a four-ring knuckleduster doubling as a handgrip. The knuckle-bow folded upward beneath the frame to provide a compact weapon. Most of the guns were made in Belgium or France and accepted 6mm pinfire cartridges, though other chamberings are known. Most of the genuine articles are marked L. DOLNE INVR. on the frame, but several have been seen with the crowned 'ML' of Manufacture Liégeoise d'Armes à Feu, and many other copies were made.

Knuckleduster guns were popular in Europe until 1914. The Delhaxhe design was clearly influenced by the Apache, but had an open-top frame and a fixed three-ring bow linking the trigger guard with the fixed bar grip. Its knife blade swivelled laterally to project beneath the butt when required.

The idea was resurrected by the British during the Second World War, when, in the spring of 1942, the staff of the Royal Small Arms Factory at Enfield Lock prepared the 'Pistol, Revolver, 9mm D.D.(E.) 3313': Design Department, Enfield, drawing No. 3313. This was a refined Dolne Apache with a folding three-ring knuckle-bow, a folding trigger, a swivelling blade on the left side of the frame and an internal hammer. The six-chamber cylinder accepted 9mm Parabellum cartridges, making the gun much more useful than the earlier knuckleduster revolvers had been. A few guns were made to D.D.(E.) 3313, but the project was abandoned in 1943. This is suspected to have been at least partly on the basis of cost, as the inexpensive single-shot .45 Liberator (q.v.) had been made in large numbers and the 9mm Sten Gun was proving a huge success.

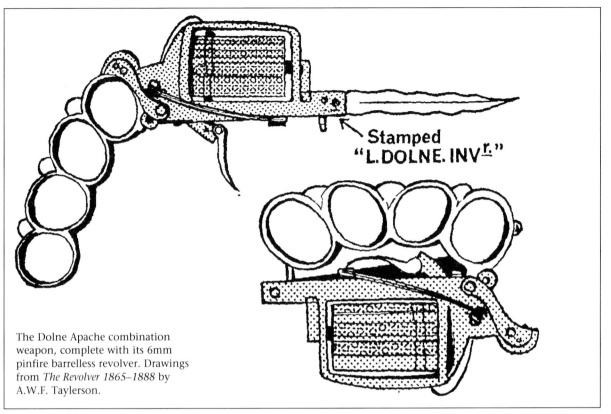

The Dolne Apache combination weapon, complete with its 6mm pinfire barrelless revolver. Drawings from *The Revolver 1865–1888* by A.W.F. Taylerson.

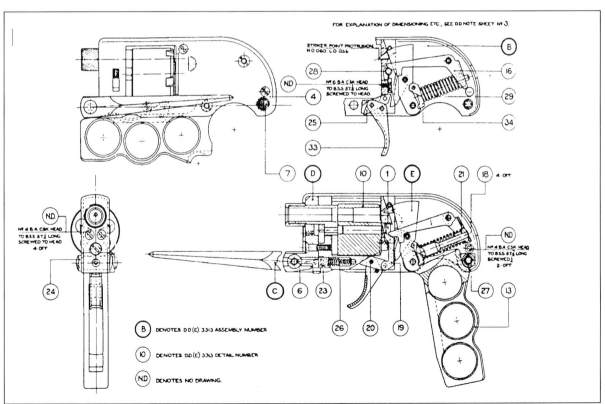

DISGUISED HANDGUNS

Pistols have been hidden in walking sticks and canes for hundreds of years, though clandestine weapons of this type are usually long arms. Flintlock pistol-canes are known, but most surviving examples are either cap-locks or chambered for metal-case cartridges. Others operate on compressed air.

BELT-BUCKLE GUNS

Only a handful of these surprise weapons are known to have been made. An occasional nineteenth-century example will be encountered, generally made with a short barrel pointing outward from an iron mounting plate on a stout leather belt. These are fired by a conventional hammer and nipple

system, the direction of the strike being lateral. A lanyard attached to the arm or leg is usually used to release the cocked hammer.

A patent granted in Britain in April 1934, to a German inventor named Goldberg, illustrated an improved belt-buckle gun based on a twelve-shot pepperbox or barrelless revolver. It is assumed that

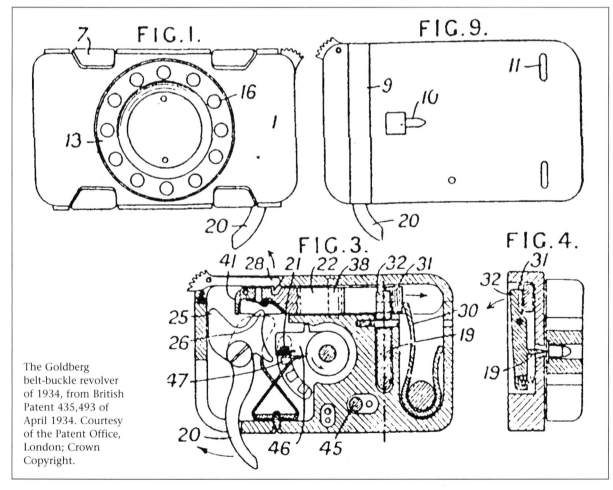

The Goldberg belt-buckle revolver of 1934, from British Patent 435,493 of April 1934. Courtesy of the Patent Office, London; Crown Copyright.

this particular personal defence weapon would have chambered weak short-case ammunition such as 4mm Übungsmunition or .22 Short rimfire, but no surviving examples have been found.

At least one 7.65mm-calibre belt buckle of a differing design was taken back to the USA in 1945 as a war trophy, and others may have been made. Its buckle-like case contains a hinged block of four barrels which springs outward when the twin release catches are pressed and automatically opens the cover plate. Each barrel is fired by an independent hammer -and-trigger mechanism, though all four can be discharged in a volley by pressing the triggers simultaneously. The unit measures about 10cm x 5cm and has an eagle-and-swastika motif dating it later than 1933. The gun was presumably made in Thuringia, centre of the German gunmaking industry, but confirmation is still lacking.

BICYCLE-HANDLEBAR GUNS

The rapid growth of bicycling in Europe in the late nineteenth century was accompanied by concern about the dangers posed by wild dogs, wolves and petty criminals. These fears created a range of defensive weapons ranging from the Puppy and Velo-Dog revolvers to the Scheintod ('simulated death') series. Few of these were secret handguns, except in the sense that they were small enough to be hidden in a pocket or purse. More intriguing were the guns which were concealed within the bicycles themselves, almost always in the handlebars, where they were instantly accessible. Originating in France and Belgium, the guns were generally tiny pinfire pepperboxes with folding triggers and bar hammers. They were held in the end of the tubular handlebars by spring latches or, much more rarely, a twist lock.

CANE, TRUNCHEON, UMBRELLA AND WALKING-STICK GUNS

Full, or rifle-length cane guns, including many pneumatic pat-

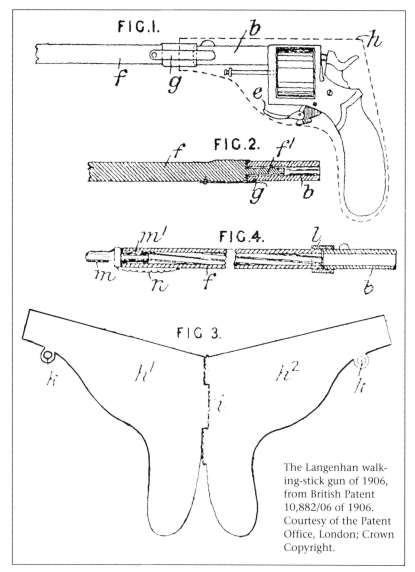

The Langenhan walking-stick gun of 1906, from British Patent 10,882/06 of 1906. Courtesy of the Patent Office, London; Crown Copyright.

terns, were made in surprisingly large numbers before 1914. Handguns are rarely found in this form, however, except for a small number of 'stick handle' pinfire pepperboxes of French or Belgian origin. These were often made with short, fixed knife blades forged integrally with the cylinder-axis pin, and may be found in canes, umbrellas and walking sticks made throughout Europe prior to the First World War. The stick body had to be removed before the revolvers could be fired.

Heinrich Langehan of Suhl was granted a British patent as late as May 1906 to protect a distinctive stick-gun. A small centre-fire revolver with a folding trigger could be attached to a solid walking-stick shaft by a peg-and-catch retainer, or held to a rifled barrel extension doubling as a stick. The revolver could be hidden inside a suitable cover until needed.

Guns will also be found in blackjacks and truncheons, often intended to appeal to the policemen of the mid nineteenth century. Pre-1850 products are generally cap-locks, including a sizeable number of English-made folding trigger underhammers marked

DAY'S PATENT; these were made in accordance with protection granted in 1823 to John Day of Barnstaple, Devon, but were probably manufactured elsewhere.

CIGARETTE AND CIGAR PISTOLS

Except for air-power dart guns, which fired hardwood needles with airgun-dart flights, the most bizarre British weapon of the Second World War was undoubtedly the Wel-Woodbine. Taking its name from the well-known cigarette, which provided disguise, the gun was little more than a 3in x ¼in tube containing a one-inch .177-calibre barrel. A detachable breech chamber was held by two tiny cross-pins. The hardened-steel projectile was fired by a pellet of priming composition, activated by a spring-loaded striker. Wel-Woodbines were rolled inside cigarette papers, care being taken to reflect the appropriate theatre of operations in the design. The muzzles were disguised with a plug of charred tobacco to suggest that they had already been lit. It was hoped that anyone to whom the packet was offered would take a pristine cigarette and leave the Wel-Woodbine to the Special Operations Executive (SOE) agent. The gun was activated by biting off the filter tip, severing the safety wire, then pressing the thumbnail on to a tiny trigger protruding through the cigarette paper.

The potential of the Wel-Woodbine is difficult to determine, as no records of success or failure have yet been found. A captive was supposed to commit suicide by shooting into the roof of the mouth, or, alternatively, to give an interrogator enough of a shock to escape. The tiny gun could even be reloaded by driving out the cross-pins holding the breech, inserting a new bullet and propellant-pellet, replacing the breech and inserting a new cork-tip safety wire.

The Wel-Cheroot, about 4½in long, was an enlarged Wel-Woodbine made in the form of a small cigar. It contained a single .22 Short rimfire cartridge activated by a lanyard, which was revealed by biting off the end of the cigar. Pulling the lanyard released the firing pin from the ball-bearing 'sear'. A few Wel-Cheroots are believed to have been issued in 1945 to the Office of Strategic Services (OSS), but no records of their use exist.

FLASHLIGHT OR TORCH PISTOLS

At least one attempt to combine a firearm and a flashlight was made by S. P. Cottrell & Son of Buffalo, New York State, in accordance with a patent granted in the USA in the summer of 1923. The seven-shot, .22 Long rimfire double-action revolver was integrated with the top of the flashlight and fired using a folding trigger on the underside of the casing. The goal was to provide a means of aiming by light beam, as the bullet would go where the light pointed, a principle revived in recent years with collimator, 'red dot' and laser sights. Cottrell two-cell flashlight-revolvers are very rare.

GLOVE PISTOLS

The US naval intelligence service procured guns of this type, patented in 1938 by S. M. Haight, though a link stretched back to the sleeve pistol (q.v.) patented in 1929 by Elek Juhasz. A single-barrel pistol attached to the back of a sturdy glove was fired simply by punching the target. This depressed a cocking plunger, projecting above the barrel, and then fired the gun in a single sweeping movement. The Mark 1 accepted .410 shotgun shells, but these were too bulky in relation to power and the Mark 2 was redesigned to use a single .38 revolver cartridge.

HAT GUNS

No book of this type would be complete without mentioning the

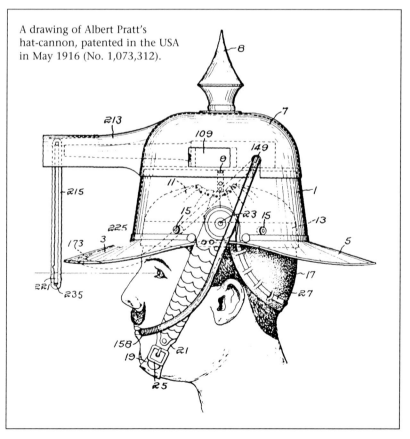

A drawing of Albert Pratt's hat-cannon, patented in the USA in May 1916 (No. 1,073,312).

life's work of the American inventor Albert Pratt of Lyndon, Vermont. Pratt patented a series of 'hat guns' in the early twentieth century, ranging from modified service revolvers to auto-loading pistols and even a small cannon. The guns were generally fired by blowtubes and, at least in the case of the US patent granted in May 1916, could be fitted into a helmet doubling as a cooking pot. The performance of these eccentric designs has, regrettably, passed unrecorded. The effects of recoil on the firer's neck muscles would have been especially interesting.

KEY PISTOLS
The true personal defence of this type is really one in which the barrel forms the body of the key to fire forward, though a few examples had self-contained short-barrelled pistols built into the key grip. These usually fire backwards, towards the holder.

Most true key pistols date from the seventeenth or eighteenth centuries, when keys were large enough to conceal a gun-lock and barrel without inviting undue comment. They are much scarcer in the nineteenth century, owing to the improvement in lock design.

PEN- AND PENCIL-GUNS
Guns of this type have a pedigree dating back to disguised cap-locks made in the second quarter of the nineteenth century. A surprising number of survivors may still be encountered, though many will be found to chamber blank- or gas cartridges instead of ball ammunition. Pen-guns are usually fired by retracting a striker until it is held against the pressure of a spring by

pivoting bars, sliding catches or button triggers. External appearance has ranged from extremely unconvincing to plausible facsimiles of the pen-styles of the day.

Among the clandestine weapons produced during the Second World War was the .22 'Experimental Firing Device, Hand Held, Welpen' of 1941, a single-shot pistol disguised as a fountain pen. Only about 100 were made in the Welwyn research establishment in Hertfordshire, England, before the project was abandoned in favour of the similar (but slimmer) Enpen.

Designed by the staff of the Royal Small Arms Factory in Enfield, the 'Auxiliary Firing Device, Hand Held, Enpen Mark I' was made in quantity in 1944. It was little more than a short tube containing a bolt-like firing pin, locked in place by two small ball bearings. A thin rod projected between the ball bearings, keeping the bolt in its cocked position until retracted by pulling the pocket-clip up and back. This removed the support behind the ball bearings, which moved inward to release the bolt and fire the cartridge. The Enpen was designed to be thrown away after use. However, a reloadable blank-firing version was made for training, and an improved Mark II could be reloaded by unscrewing the barrel section. An essentially similar .38-calibre pen-pistol was chambered for tear-gas cartridges.

The OSS had the single-shot .22 Stinger, which was comparable with the Enpen except that the .22 Short cartridge was integral with the fabric of the weapon. The Stinger was fired by raising a short lever set into the body, which

armed the striker. Replacing the lever released the striker and fired the cartridge. The gun, which was only about 3½in long and weighed less than half an ounce, was then simply thrown away.

PIPE PISTOLS
The shape of a smoker's pipe lends itself naturally to concealment of a small handgun. Few seem to have been made commercially; they were usually produced on an occasional basis. A typical specimen, chambered for the .22 Short rimfire cartridge, contains a spring-loaded striker travelling in a short 'L' slot in the pipe body. The gun is cocked simply by retracting the striker arm and turning it through 90° to enter the shorter slot-arm. Firing is simply a matter of easing the striker arm over until it flies down the long slot arm under spring pressure to hit the rim of the cartridge.

More sophisticated designs incorporated a retractable 'straight line' striker and a rocking bar or button trigger. The principle was revived during the Second World War, as the OSS apparently used a few Welwyn-made .22 pipe-pistols. These were locked by a bayonet-catch mechanism.

POCKET-WATCH GUNS
The only known combinations of this type were the work of Leonard Woods of St Louis, Missouri. The single-shot watch-gun patented in September 1913 contained a single central barrel masquerading as the winder stem, and a simple hammer mechanism. It was loaded by unscrewing the barrel, then fired by pressing back the slider above the barrel to activate the hammer. Woods subsequently produced a

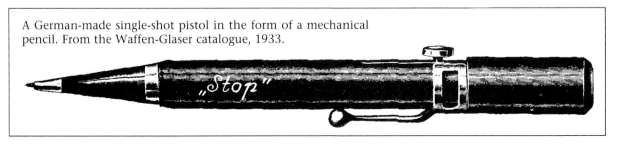

A German-made single-shot pistol in the form of a mechanical pencil. From the Waffen-Glaser catalogue, 1933.

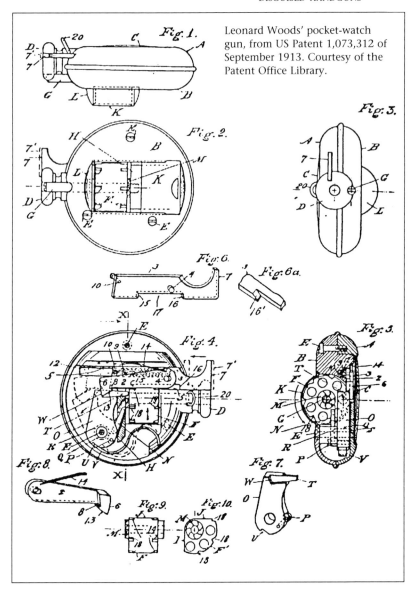

Leonard Woods' pocket-watch gun, from US Patent 1,073,312 of September 1913. Courtesy of the Patent Office Library.

often bearing three-digit serial numbers.

The uniquely Scottish sporran could be considered as a purse by stretching the imagination. The novelist Sir Walter Scott, in his book *Rob Roy* (1817), described one containing a flintlock pistol; another is still owned by the National Museum of Scotland in Edinburgh.

SLEEVE PISTOLS

One of the few attempts to develop a self-defence gun in this category was made by Elek Juhasz, who was granted an appropriate US Patent in August 1929. The barrel of his single-shot pistol, attached to the forearm by elasticated straps, unscrewed to load a .30-calibre centre-fire cartridge. The spring-loaded striker was cocked manually and then fired by a lanyard running from the trigger to a ring slipped around a finger. The firer only had to raise his hand to fire the gun, a potentially risky action which undoubtedly contributed to the universal lack of interest shown in sleeve guns.

STIRRUP PISTOLS

Two of these, a matched pair, were sold at auction in Toronto in 1935 from the collection of the noted antiquary Charles Daly, but there is nothing to suggest that they were unique. Apparently made in France in the 1860s and found in Bordeaux in 1917, the two-shot stirrups accompanied a breastplate mounting no fewer than nineteen pinfire pistol barrels which could be fired in volleys of four or five shots. One stirrup faced backwards, discouraging pursuit, with the other pointed forward to assist an attack. They were fired with lanyards.

TOOL GUNS

Pistols have occasionally been built into tools, particularly hammers and wrenches. Most have had the handles or hafts altered to conceal a single barrel chambered

repeating .22 Short rimfire version (patented in the USA in August 1915) with a seven-shot cylinder, but there is no evidence that it was ever made in quantity.

PURSE PISTOLS

Pistols became easier to build into purses, cigarette cases and wallets as they became smaller. Among the best was the 'Combination Pocket-Book & Revolver' (known in Britain as a 'Revolver Purse') patented in the autumn of 1877 by Otto Frankenau of Magdeburg, Germany. The drawings accompanying British Patent 3375/1877 illustrate a pepperbox, but the finalised version incorporated a small 5mm six-shot double-action pinfire revolver. The gun was hidden inside a two-compartment sheet metal case, one portion of which could be opened to contain coins. The trigger could be unfolded and pressed to fire the gun, automatically opening the muzzle flap before the shot was fired. Frankenau purse-pistols were about 100mm long, 62mm high and 30mm thick. Production seems to have been substantial, survivors for a small rim- or centre-fire cartridge. Pivoting- bar or button triggers release spring-loaded strikers, though a few slam-fire designs are known. There is no evidence that many tool-guns were made in quantity, or that established gunsmiths were involved.

An exception is the telescopelike Buco, which consists of a short, large-diameter sheet metal tube containing a coil spring, the firing mechanism and a small-diameter barrel. The knurled cap is rotated until two orange or red marks align, then removed to gain

access to the breech. A special 10.6mm cartridge is inserted into the chamber, the barrel is pulled forward until the sear engages, and the end-cap is replaced. The Buco can be fired merely by pressing the button protruding through the casing, which pivots the sear to release

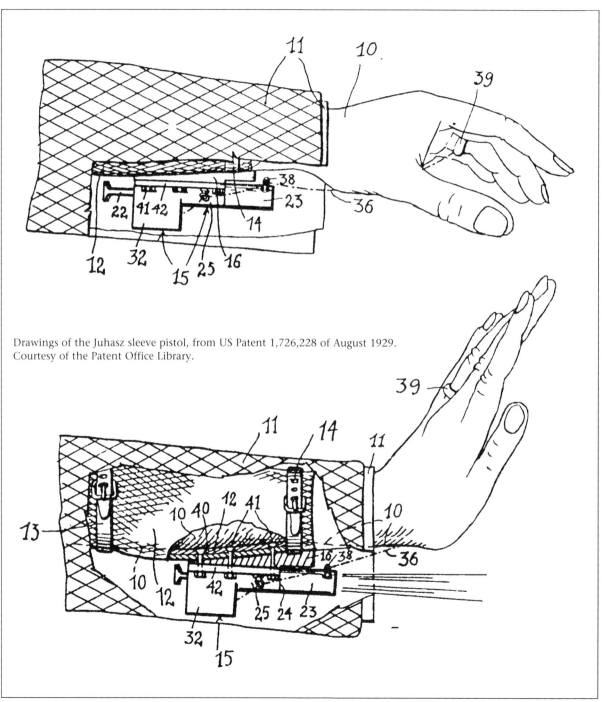

Drawings of the Juhasz sleeve pistol, from US Patent 1,726,228 of August 1929. Courtesy of the Patent Office Library.

the barrel. The barrel then flies backwards under the influence of the spring until the primer of the cartridge is slammed against a pin fixed on the inside of the end cap.

The telescope-guns marked BUCO/D.R.G.M. are suspected to have been by Richard Bornmüller & Co. of Suhl. The special ammunition has not yet been conclusively identified, but was probably loaded with a gas charge; lightweight construction suggests that the Buco could not have withstood the pressures developed by ball cartridges.

A single-shot 'squeezer' pistol, patented in February 1905 by George Webber of Chicago, could be classified as a tool by stretching the imagination, though which particular tool it represented is debatable. The gun consisted of a tube forming the barrel and breech, a hemispherical rubber palm rest and a sliding operating collar. It was held in the hand with the rubber pad against the base of the thumb and the muzzle projecting between the index and second fingers. Squeezing the fingers inward slid the collar down the tube, cocking and ultimately releasing the striker to fire the gun. The barrel unscrewed from the breech to load.

TRAP GUNS

The range of firearms of this type extends from guns built into man- and animal-traps to simple drop-weight alarms. Though few can be truly classed as handguns, an important exception was the Game-Shooter. Patented in the USA in June 1859 by John Couch and Henry North, this was basically a six-barrel pepperbox with a single nipple. The barrel cluster could be slid forward against the pressure of a spring in the central axis-tube until it was held open by the sear. A volley of shots was fired by pulling on the muzzle rod or pressing the trigger, which enabled the trap gun to double as a personal defence if required. The Game-Shooter was supposedly hung from a branch, fence or similar anchor by a cord attached to the backstrap ring. Another cord was run from the muzzle rod to bait. When an animal tugged the bait strongly enough, the muzzle rod released the sear, the barrel cluster sprang backwards and the gun fired. The Game-Shooter is said to have been very popular in Australia, to protect sheep against wild dogs (dingos) and discourage kangaroos. It also made a handy booby-trap.

The earliest guns, with a distinctive cylindrical appearance and an unprotected trigger, were made by North & Savage in Middletown, Connecticut, in 1859–60. Work seems to have been stopped by the Civil War, but was resumed about 1866, by which time North & Savage had become the Savage Revolving Firearms Company. Post-war guns had flat-sided frames, sheathed triggers and a prominent top-latch to hold the barrels shut. Though most were cap-locks, a few chambered rimfire ammunition. Work seems to have ceased about 1870.

WHIP PISTOLS

These are uncommon, but usually consist of nothing other than a short tubular barrel/breech assembly which can be detached from the body of the whip when required. Cap-lock and cartridge versions have been reported, normally fired by a combination of a retractable spring-loaded striker and a rocking bar or button trigger. Individual construction varies greatly. No individual gunmaker has yet been identified with specialisation in this particular endeavour, though many surviving examples seem to display Birmingham proof marks.

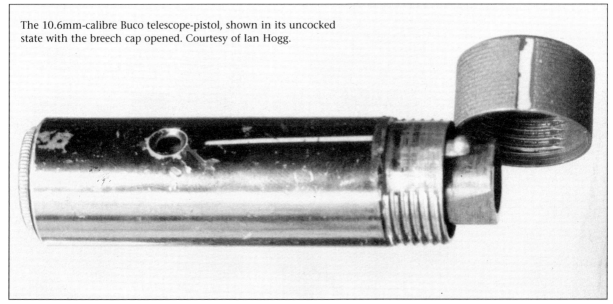

The 10.6mm-calibre Buco telescope-pistol, shown in its uncocked state with the breech cap opened. Courtesy of Ian Hogg.

MULTI-SHOT DESIGNS

Another form of secrecy was provided by guns which externally resembled single-shot patterns but were actually capable of firing more than once. The earliest of these originated in the days of match- and wheel-locks; the first datable reference to *Klotzbüchsen* (from *Klötze*, small leaden balls) is to be found in a fifteenth-century manuscript in the Stadtsbibliothek in Vienna.

SUPERIMPOSED LOADS

Multi-barrel pistols openly advertised their construction, but the same could not be said of guns which relied on multiple locks (or alternatively a single sliding lock) to fire superimposed charges from the same barrel. A major failing of this kind of secret weapon was an unfortunate tendency to fire the shots in a volley, generally because the wad between the charges failed to seal the bore.

This did not stop inventors striving for perfection. Jover & Belton briefly made a pistol with a sliding flintlock and a detachable seven-shot chamber, Auguste Robert made a multi-shot pistol with multiple cap-lock hammers beneath the breech, and a Frenchman named Ramel made a gun loaded with a special four-shot cartridge.

The most successful of the superimposed-charge guns were made in North America in accordance with patents granted in February 1859 to John Walch and in October 1860 to John Lindsay. Walch's guns were ten- and twelve-shot revolvers, made by the J. P. Lindsay Manufacturing Company of New Haven, Connecticut. Armed with this experience, Lindsay subsequently made two-shot rifle-muskets externally resembling the 1855-type regulation Springfield. These were intended to persuade Indians into attacking in the belief that reloading was under way. The rifle-muskets were briefly successful enough to encourage the manufacture of a two-shot 'Young America' pistol.

THE CAP-LOCK PEPPERBOXES

The pepperbox and the revolver, with multiple barrels and multiple-chamber cylinders respectively, were the first handguns to be not only easy to conceal but also truly useful. The major improvement on the tiny cap-locks was nothing other than the ability to fire more than one shot before reloading was needed. Multi-shot capability encouraged the use of handguns in attack as well as defence, and

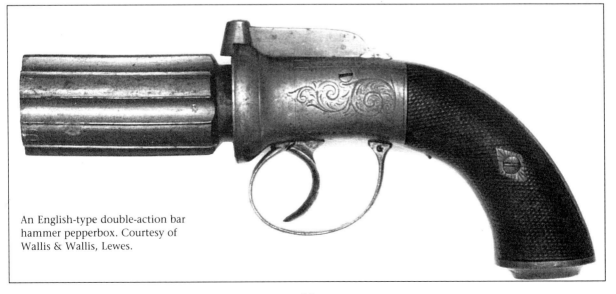

An English-type double-action bar hammer pepperbox. Courtesy of Wallis & Wallis, Lewes.

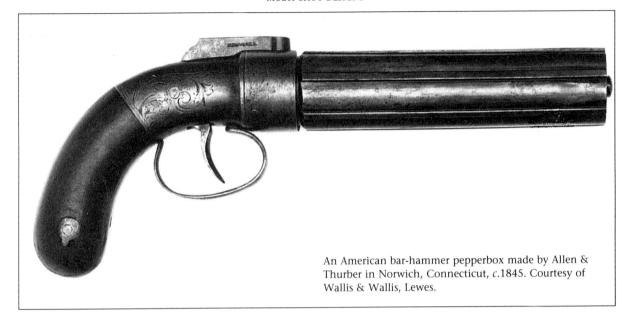

An American bar-hammer pepperbox made by Allen & Thurber in Norwich, Connecticut, c.1845. Courtesy of Wallis & Wallis, Lewes.

brought an important change in the regard in which guns of this type were held.

The pepperbox descended from the multi-barrel pistols pioneered in the earliest days of firearms history. Flintlock examples were in vogue in the last quarter of the eighteenth century. Among the best-known are guns made by John Twigg of London, who traded on his own account from 1755 until 1788, and by an otherwise obscure French gunsmith named Mairet. Thomas Ketland of Birmingham (who usually marked his wares 'London'), Henry Nock of London, and William Wilson of London are all known to have made guns of this type.

Twigg's pepperboxes generally had six or seven barrels, mounted around a solid central core serving as the axis-pin for the barrel block. Each barrel had its own touch hole but was served by a single cock and frizzen. A box was sometimes attached to the frizzen to feed a predetermined measure of priming powder into the pan each time a barrel was rotated into position and the cock had been thumbed back.

A few guns, however, including many of Mairet's, had six barrels surrounding a central seventh which doubled as the axis pin. Firing the central barrel presented a problem, as it could not have a touch hole of its own. The popular solution was to pour a double charge into the central barrel so that half flowed through a narrow connecting channel into the sixth barrel in the outer ring. The sixth and seventh barrels, therefore, fired virtually simultaneously.

Flintlock pepperboxes were heavy in relation to their calibre, balanced clumsily, and remained uncommon. Not until the percussion cap was perfected in the 1820s did this situation change greatly. Caps allowed each barrel to be primed separately, and ignition was reasonably certain as long as the caps could be held efficiently on the nipples. Cap-lock pepperboxes were also much more compact than their flintlock ancestors. The barrel clusters of the earliest cap-lock designs were rotated manually and fired by single-acting trigger systems. The guns were simple, acceptably sturdy, easy to make, and accurate enough at short range to be useful in a fight. However, keeping the size of the barrel cluster within acceptable bounds restricted the diameter of the bore and thus the 'hitting power' of the ball. Most purchasers

regarded this disadvantage as a small price to pay for additional shots.

Short-barrel guns were occasionally prone to 'chain fire', discharging all their barrels simultaneously when either the flash of a cap radiated outwards to other flash holes or flame from the firing chamber ignited its neighbours. The phenomena could be avoided by erecting fences between the nipples and sealing each chamber with a greased wad above the projectile. They were more prevalent in short-chamber revolvers than in long-barrel pepperboxes.

Pepperboxes were made in large numbers in Britain and Europe in the middle of the nineteenth century, before being swept away by cap-lock and pinfire revolvers. Several gunmakers showed them in the Great Exhibition of 1851, including Brooks & Son of Birmingham; John R. Cooper & Company of Birmingham; Joseph Lang of Haymarket, London (the 'Turnover'); Charles Osborne of Birmingham; Westley Richards & Son of Birmingham; William & John Rigby of Dublin; Tipping & Lawden of Birmingham; and Edward Trulock & Son of Dublin.

Typical of the British designs were those promoted by Charles

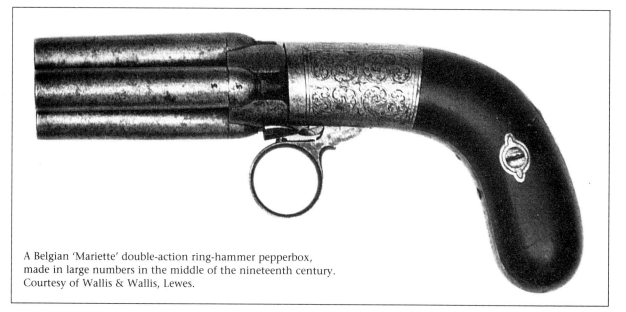

A Belgian 'Mariette' double-action ring-hammer pepperbox, made in large numbers in the middle of the nineteenth century. Courtesy of Wallis & Wallis, Lewes.

Smith, active in Whittall Street, Birmingham, in 1845–52, who obtained an English patent in 1845 to protect (among other things) priming magazines and a double-action pepperbox pistol. As late as 1860, gunsmith Robert Hughes of Birmingham was advertising himself as a manufacturer of 'Every Description of Military and Sporting Rifles, Single and Double Breech and Muzzle-loading Guns, Revolvers and every other kind of Pistols'. The illustrations accompanying this particular advertisement included pepperboxes.

Although many cap-locks of this class were made in France and Belgium, notably in the Liége district, they were eventually superseded by pinfires. The best-known of the Continental pepperboxes is the Mariette, allegedly developed in the 1830s by a French gunmaker of the same name, which was customarily distinguished by a double-action ring trigger.

Cap-lock pepperboxes were also made in the USA. The first American designs were manually rotated, but the introduction of the Paterson Colt revolvers persuaded enterprising gunsmiths to revolve the cylinders mechanically.

The guns made by Barton &

Benjamin Darling, initially in Shrewsbury, Massachusetts, are generally regarded as the earliest of all the self-rotating pepperboxes. The first guns had thumb triggers on top of the butt, but were rapidly superseded by a conventional design. Production of Darling pepperboxes was never large enough to attract attention in North America, and the grant of the patent in April 1836, after Colt's, undermines the claim that the Darlings perfected the mechanically rotated cylinder.

Much more successful than the single-action Darling was the double-action or 'self-cocking' pepperbox patented by Ethan Allen in November 1837. The guns were made by Allen & Thurber in Grafton, Massachusetts (until 1842), Norwich, Connecticut (1842–7), and then in the small Masschusetts town of Worcester. Later guns were made by Allen & Wheelock, successors to Allen & Thurber in the mid 1850s. The Allens were made in several differing patterns, typically .32 or .36-calibre five- or six-shot smooth-bores with bar hammers and double-action triggers. The best of them were made before the granting of an improved patent in April 1845, when ribbed barrel flut-

ing, nipple shields, engraving and silvered escutcheons were gradually abandoned in the face of strong competition from other American gunmakers. Six-shot guns gave way to five-shot types, which were smaller and lighter, and a few were even made with ring triggers in an attempt to reduce manufacturing costs.

Ten North American Pepperbox Makers

Bacon & Company, Norwich, Connecticut
  Single-action, underhammer type.
Blunt & Syms, New York City
  Double action, underhammer type.
George Leonard, Charlestown, Maryland, and Shrewsbury, Massachusetts.
  Double-action, ring-trigger pattern with fixed barrels.
Manhattan Fire Arms Company, Newark, New Jersey
  Double-action, bar hammer.
William Marston, Newark, New Jersey, and New York City
  Double-action, bar hammer.
Pecare & Smith, New York City
  Double-action, folding or ring triggers.
Robbins & Lawrence, Windsor, Vermont
  Double-action, ring trigger.

Stocking & Company, Worcester, Massachusetts

Single-action, with an extended hammer spur and a spurred trigger guard.

Union Arms Company, Hartford,

Connecticut

Double-action, bar hammer.

Washington Arms Company, Washington, D.C.

Double-action.

The marks of retailers, sporting-goods promoters and other agencies will often be found on European and American-made pepper-boxes. A list of more than 130 British retailers was given by

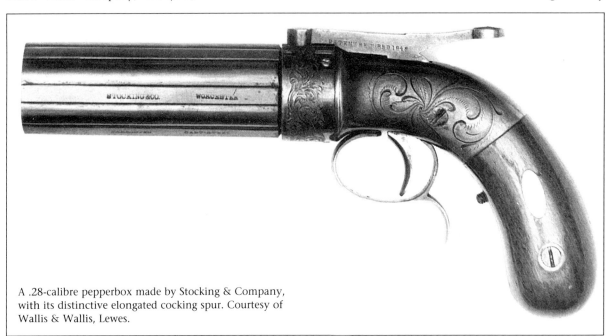

A .28-calibre pepperbox made by Stocking & Company, with its distinctive elongated cocking spur. Courtesy of Wallis & Wallis, Lewes.

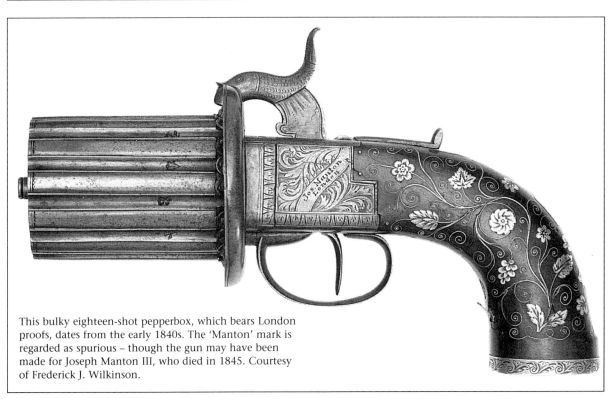

This bulky eighteen-shot pepperbox, which bears London proofs, dates from the early 1840s. The 'Manton' mark is regarded as spurious – though the gun may have been made for Joseph Manton III, who died in 1845. Courtesy of Frederick J. Wilkinson.

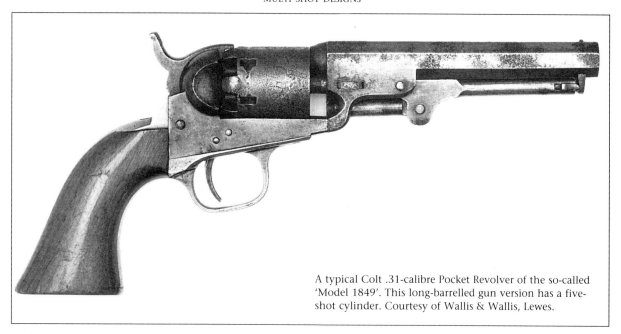

A typical Colt .31-calibre Pocket Revolver of the so-called 'Model 1849'. This long-barrelled gun version has a five-shot cylinder. Courtesy of Wallis & Wallis, Lewes.

Taylerson, Andrews & Frith in *The Revolver, 1818–1865* (1968). In the USA, John G. Bolen of New York City sold pepperboxes as 'Life and Property Preservers'. Bolen specialised in cased pairs; two identical guns, or one large and one small. As the guns were purchased from several differing sources, they may not match exactly.

THE CAP-LOCK REVOLVERS

Although several attempts were made to develop satisfactory revolving-chamber pistols in the flintlock period, culminating in the Collier design, the credit for perfecting the mechanically-operated revolver is rightfully due to Samuel Colt. Colt's first design was the subject of an English patent granted in October 1835, comparable US protection following in January 1836. The destruction of the Patent Office in Washington shortly after the grant of Colt's patent has, however, clouded much of the story.

Colt claimed that his handguns eased loading problems and could be fired more rapidly than single-shot pistols. The advantages over manually-operated pepperboxes were gained simply by linking the hammer and cylinder-rotating pawl so that the cylinder rotated automatically when the hammer was thumbed back to full cock. The cylinder was locked by a bolt in the frame as the hammer fell.

In 1835 Colt formed the Patent Arms Manufacturing Company to promote his revolvers and revolver-rifles, the guns being made in a factory in Paterson, New Jersey. The trigger of the earliest Paterson Colts sprang down beneath the frame as the hammer was cocked. The handguns were made in several sizes, but a tiny .28-calibre pocket revolver remained a solitary prototype.

The Paterson venture failed in 1843, and it must have seemed that the Colt revolver would simply fade from the scene. However, the success of the .44 Walker Colt in the Mexican War and the adoption of the Dragoon Colt by the US Army brought a reversal in fortune. Military success suggested that smaller revolvers would have commercial appeal, and the .31-calibre pocket Colt, or 'Baby Dragoon', was announced in 1848. More than 15,000 had been made by 1851, distinguished by barrels as short as 3in and square-back trigger guards.

With the exception of the last few to be made, the pocket revolvers lacked rammers. The absence of a rammer meant reloading by substituting cylinders, though the axis pin could be used as a rudimentary rammer once the cylinder had been detached. This was a serious drawback in a military weapon, but of no importance in a gun which would only occasionally be used in anger.

An astute publicist, Colt capitalised on the use of his revolvers in battle by rolling a decorative 'Texas Rangers and Indians' scene into the outer surface of the cylinders of the earliest pocket revolvers. After about 1850, however, this was replaced by a stagecoach robbery. The Baby Dragoon was replaced by the popular .31 Pocket Revolver of which 325,000 were made, including about 11,000 in London, the last being sold in 1873.

These 1850-type .31 revolvers had five- or, more rarely, six-shot cylinders. Barrels could be as short as 3in, though they were generally somewhat longer. The cylinder invariably displayed the stagecoach robbery scene, the grip straps could be silver plated and engraving was often evident. The

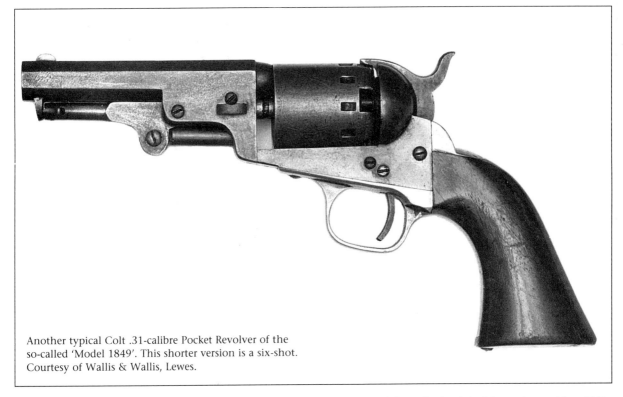

Another typical Colt .31-calibre Pocket Revolver of the so-called 'Model 1849'. This shorter version is a six-shot. Courtesy of Wallis & Wallis, Lewes.

earliest guns had a notably cramped trigger guard, but this was soon changed.

A short-barrel 'Wells Fargo' .31 Colt was also made in small numbers. It lacked a rammer and could be concealed very easily, though the small-diameter bullet was a notoriously poor man-stopper. This was sufficient to restrict the utility of the guns to 'back up' for more powerful weapons.

COLT'S FIRST RIVALS
The success of the cap-lock Colts encouraged rivalry. Among the most efficient of the earliest challengers was the Wesson & Leavitt revolver, made by the Massachusetts Arms Company of Chicopee Falls. This gun was based on a manually-rotated cylinder patented by Daniel Leavitt in April 1837 and a mechanically-rotated improvement posthumously credited to Edwin Wesson in 1859. The earliest Wesson & Leavitts rotated their cylinders with bevel gears. Gigantic .40-calibre six-shot army revolvers were accompanied by

.31-calibre six-shot Belt Models, about 1,000 being made in 1850–1. The barrel, sometimes as short as 3in, was held to the cylinder axis pin by a swivel latch. Reloading was simply a matter of pressing the latch, raising the barrel, and pulling the cylinder off the axis pin.

A controversial extension of his original patent until 1857 allowed Colt to sue the Massachusetts Arms Company for infringement. The trial gripped New England for weeks as the flamboyant Rufus Choate, for the defendants, traded insults with the dogged Edwin Dickinson for Colt. Dickinson and Colt won, all but breaking the Massachusetts Arms Company financially. The offending mechanically operated Wesson & Leavitts were replaced by simpler .31 Belt Models, relying on manually rotated cylinders and a locking latch in the trigger guard ahead of the trigger. Almost all had Maynard Tape Primers, but only about 1,000 were made in 1851–7.

The Massachusetts Arms Company also made a tiny .28-calibre

Pocket Model revolver with a 2½in or 3in octagonal barrel, Maynard Tape Primers, and a single nipple mounted on the frame. The manually rotated cylinders of the earliest examples were locked by a button inside the trigger guard.

In August 1853, Joshua Stevens patented an attempt to circumvent Colt's patents. The hammer had to be thumb-cocked, operating the Maynard primer; pressing the trigger then unlocked, rotated and secured the cylinder, finally tripping the hammer at the end of the stroke. An improved Stevens action, patented in January 1855, relied on the trigger to rotate the cylinder before the hammer was cocked. The Massachusetts Arms Company made about 350 Belt and Pocket Model revolvers embodying the original Stevens system, then about 1,500 large-frame .28 or .31 Pocket Models with the 1855-type action. These guns had 3–3½in round or octagonal barrels.

Guns resembling the Wesson & Leavitts were made by the Springfield Arms Company around a

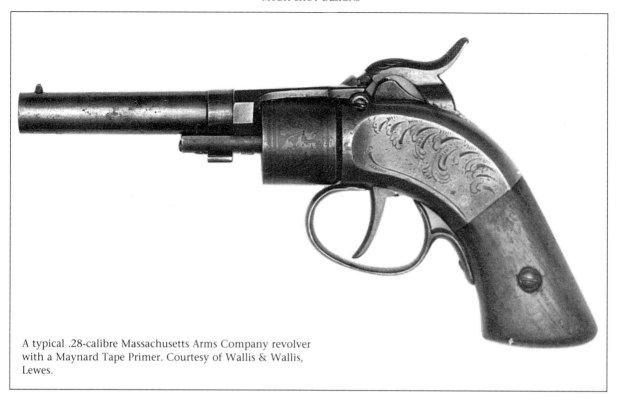

A typical .28-calibre Massachusetts Arms Company revolver with a Maynard Tape Primer. Courtesy of Wallis & Wallis, Lewes.

hammer-rotated cylinder patented by company superintendent James Warner in July 1851. The all-metal, .40-calibre six-shot 'Dragoon Pistols' were originally distinguished by their nipple shield and a safety gate; later examples had conventional wooden grips. Next came the Jaquith Patent Belt Model, though acknowledgement to a patent granted to Elijah Jaquith in July 1838 was little more than a ploy to mislead Colt.

These .31-calibre six-shot revolvers, with 4–6in round barrels, were superseded by the similar Warner Patent Belt Model. Warner-patent guns combined a modified Jaquith-pattern cylinder-rotating hand and a separate locking bolt. A two-trigger variant appeared in 1852. The hammer was cocked manually, the front trigger was pressed to index the cylinder, and the rear lever was pressed to trip the hammer.

The cylinders of the .28-calibre six-shot Warner Patent Pocket Models were rotated by the hammer, a ring trigger, or the two-trig-

ger system, even though production scarcely exceeded 1,500. Some barrels were rifled, but others were smooth-bored.

James Warner continued to make pocketable cap-lock revolvers after the Springfield Arms Company collapsed in 1868. The .28 pocket model was originally made with a 3in octagonal barrel, but a round barrel was substituted after 1,000 guns had been made and the calibre changed to .31. Production continued until Warner's death in 1870, total output approaching 10,000. Barrel lengths were customarily between 2⅝in and 4in.

THE ROOT-PATTERN COLT
The original pocket-size Colts were rapidly superseded by the Model 1855 or 'Root Pattern'. This took its name from Elisha Root, superintendent of the Hartford factory, whose design was intended to eliminate the major weaknesses of open-frame construction. The Root revolvers had solid frames, sheathed triggers

and a cranked side-hammer mounted externally on the right side of the frame. This construction allowed the cylinder axis pin to enter from the rear. However, though the Root-patent revolvers were sturdy and durable, Colt's master patent expired almost as soon as production had begun and Root died unexpectedly soon afterwards. The removal of protection exposed the Colts to competition, particularly from cheaper (if usually inferior) categories of personal-defence weapon. Only about 40,000 .28 and .31 Root-type Colts were made from 1855 until 1870. The barrels, usually round, measured 3½in or 4½in, and a log-cabin-and-Indian design was rolled into the cylinder.

THE FLOOD GATES OPEN
No sooner had Colt's master patent expired in 1857 than the Massachusetts Arms Company began production of a revolver with a simple hammer-rotated cylinder. About 2,300 were made, including

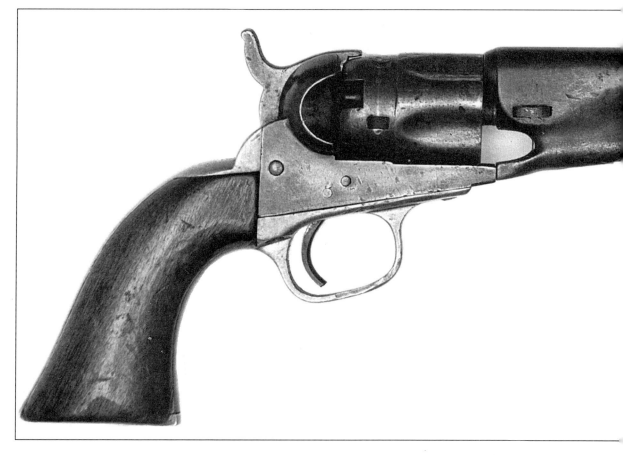

a few hundred conversions based on the improved Stevens action, but the quantities were not large enough to make an impact commercially.

The Massachusetts Arms Company then decided to make British Beaumont-Adams revolvers under licence, but only 1,000 .36-calibre six-shot Navy and 4,800 .31 five-shot Pocket Models had been made when the Civil War began.

Eli Whitney, who had supported Colt in the 1840s, was another of the major gunmakers attracted to the revolver. In August 1854, Whitney patented a ring-trigger design with a frame made 'all in one piece, with a top bar, not only to strengthen the frame but also to serve as a foil with a comb of the hammer to strike against to prevent battering the cones [nipples]'. Only a few of these guns were made, however, as work concentrated on a ring-trigger revolver

patented by Fordyce Beals in September 1856.

The 'Walking Beam Whitney', as the quirky Beals design became known, was cocked manually. Pushing the trigger lever forward rotated the cylinder with the operating bar; pulling the trigger back locked the cylinder in place and then released the hammer. Only a few of these distinctive solid-frame ring-trigger cap locks were made. The .28 version is particularly rare, most survivors being .31-calibre five-chamber guns.

The first pocketable revolver made by Remington was a five-shot .31 patented in 1856–7 by Fordyce Beals. About 5,000 guns were made from 1857 until work stopped in 1861–2. The first Remington-Beals had an external arm and pawl actuating the cylinder, the second version of 1858–60 relied on a disc-and-pawl mechanism, and the essentially similar

third type had a lever rammer patented in the summer of 1858. Barrels were 3in or 4in long, and weights ranged from 12oz to 14oz.

The perfected Remington pocket revolver was patented by Joseph Rider in 1858–9. This five-shot .31 gun, with a 3in barrel, weighed 10oz. Instantly recognisable by its 'mushroom' cylinder and solid frame, the Remington-Rider was offered in blue or nickel plate, with grips of gutta-percha, ivory or mother-of-pearl. These Rider revolvers were surprisingly popular; about 100,000 were made, though new guns were still being stored in Remington's warehouses in 1886.

Remington cap-locks were second only to Colt in popularity during the American Civil War. The .44-calibre revolvers purchased by the Federal government were supplemented by about 8,000 .36 six-shot New Model Belt Revolvers

The 1862-type streamlined Colt .36 New Model Police Revolver was distinguished by its fluted cylinder and creeping rammer. Courtesy of Wallis & Wallis, Lewes.

with 6½in octagonal barrels. Most purchasers preferred the double-action version. The finish was blue, nickel, or a nickel-plated frame with a blued barrel, though specially engraved guns could be supplied to order.

The .36 five-shot New Model Police Revolvers were essentially similar to the New Model Belt type, but their barrels could be as short as 3½in; the shortest guns weighed just 21oz. About 18,000 were made in 1863–70, though guns were still in store in 1886.

The .31 five-shot New Model Pocket Remington revolver, of which 27,500 were made in this period, had a sheath trigger but was otherwise built on classically Remington lines. Made with octagonal barrels measuring 3½in or 4½in, it weighed 14–16oz.

The Civil War provided such a bonanza that many new revolvers appeared. Among them were guns based on patents granted to Ethan Allen in January and December 1857. Made by Allen & Wheelock, the sturdy revolver indexed its cylinder with commendable precision and had a projection on the cylinder to minimise fouling around the axis pin.

Guns were made in many configurations by Allen & Wheelock of Worcester, Massachusetts. They included tiny five-shot .31- and .34-calibre double-action, bar-hammer revolvers with cranked side-hammers, allowing the axis pin to enter the cylinder through the rear of the frame. The method used to rotate the cylinder was unique, comprising a transverse bar in the recoil shield (rotated by the hammer) and a corresponding groove cut across the back of the cylinder. Side-hammer guns were made in .28, .31, .34 (five shots apiece) and a six-shot .36; barrels were octagonal, 2½–8in long, and the rammer formed a substantial part of the trigger guard. Production totalled about 4,000, .31 examples being most common. A few centre-hammer derivatives were subsequently chambered for rimfire cartridges, but their bored-through cylinders infringed the Rollin White patent controlled by Smith & Wesson and production was soon stopped.

Allen & Wheelock also developed a single-action .36-calibre sheath trigger revolver during the Civil War, allegedly for the police department of Providence, Rhode Island. Some examples may be encountered with barrels as short as 3in, suiting them to concealment.

THE NEW MODEL CAP-LOCK COLTS

Samuel Colt died in 1862, soon after the introduction of the first of the new streamlined cap-locks, the .44 New Model Army Revolver or Model 1860. The new weapons were purchased in large quantities by the Federal government, assuring long-term success. Among the derivatives of the .44 New Model Army Colt were the five-shot .36 New Model Police and .36 'New Model Pocket Pistol of Navy Caliber', introduced commercially in 1861. About 47,000 were made in a single number series. They were practically identical, though New Model Police revolvers had fluted cylinders and creeping rammers instead of plain cylinders and hinged rammers. Their barrels measured 4½–6½in, though 50 Police revolvers were made in 1862 with plain 3½in barrels. The brass rammer, carried separately, was pushed through the aperture in the barrel shroud.

Police and Pocket Navy revolvers were rarely engraved, though a few had 'Tiffany Grips', cast from the designs of John Ward for Tiffany & Company of New York. An eagle-and-justice motif, a Civil War battle scene, and the US or Mexican eagles were among the most popular.

Copies of the Colt Revolver, 1861–70

Note: many of these guns will be marked by wholesalers such as Henry Dimick & Co.; Fitch & Waldo; B. J. Hart & Brother; Tomes, Melvain & Company; the Union Arms Company; or the Western Arms Company.

Bacon Manufacturing Co., Norwich, Connecticut

A .31 cap-lock distinguished by a ball catch on the rammer head. Made until 1867, then superseded by the Hopkins & Allen version (q.v.)

Hopkins & Allen, Norwich, Connecticut

1) A .31 cap-lock. A post-1867 version of the .31 Bacon pattern, with a detachable side-plate on the frame and an improved three-piece rammer.

2) Dictator. A .36 cap-lock.

3) New Dictator. A .38 rimfire.

Manhattan Fire Arms Co., Newark, New Jersey

1) A .31 cap-lock made in accordance with a patent granted to Joseph Gruler and August Rebety

in 1859, distinguished by safety notches between each pair of cylinder-stop notches and detachable frame-side plates. Sometimes marked by the spurious 'London Pistol Company'. Discontinued in 1864.

2) A .36 cap-lock.

Metropolitan Fire Arms Co., New York City

1) A five-shot .36 cap-lock with a pivoted rammer, based on the Colt New Model Police revolver of 1862.

2) A six-shot .36 cap-lock with a pivoted rammer, based on the five-shot .36 New Model Police ('M1862'). Sometimes found with a naval scene, the Battle of New Orleans, rolled into the cylinder.

Nepperhan Fire Arms Co., Yonkers, New York

A five-shot .31 cap-lock with a detachable side plate.

Very few copies of the Colt equalled the quality of Hartford-made guns, nor did they show originality. A notable exception was the double-action revolver patented in 1860–3 by James Cooper of Pittsburgh. Cooper revolvers were easily identified by the trigger lever, which lay well forward in the guard to allow sufficient travel to rotate the hammer mechanically. However, the guns were otherwise easily confused with the cap-lock Colts of similar size. A hundred guns were made in Pittsburgh, infringing patents held by Gruler & Rebety and the luckless Manhattan Fire Arms Company. Cooper then moved to Philadelphia, where production of five-shot .31 pocket and six-shot .36 navy revolvers began immediately. Iron guards and grip straps were fitted to the first few hundred guns, brass components being used thereafter. The plain cylinders of the earliest .36 guns were replaced by a double-diameter pattern, the lower part of the frame being cut away to accept it. After more than 10,000 had been made, the .31-calibre pocket revolver gained a large-diameter cylinder with a sixth chamber. Marks on the perfected revolvers acknowledged patents granted to Stanhope Marston (1851), Josiah Ells (1854) and Charles Harris (1863), in addition to Cooper himself.

Distinctive revolvers resembling the military Savage & North pattern, apart from their sheath triggers, were made in Middletown, Connecticut, in 1862–3 in accordance with patents granted to Charles R. and Charles H. Alsop. The Alsop family held a sizeable stake in the Savage Repeating Fire-Arms Company, though the pocket revolvers seem to have been made elsewhere in New England. One particularly interesting feature of the Alsop revolver was the gas-seal, accomplished by combining sliding chambers and a cam which moved the cylinder forward over the breech when the hammer spur was pressed. Only about 800 .31- and .36-calibre guns were made prior to 1863, often with barrel lengths of merely 3in. The Alsop design was too complicated to compete with the legions of simple small-calibre cap-locks that flooded on to the market during the Civil War.

ENGLISH CAP-LOCK REVOLVERS

Although substantial numbers of pepperboxes were made in Britain in the 1840s, and even small numbers of the first Colts had been sold on the British market, little interest was evinced in the revolver until the Great Exhibition of 1851. An impressive display of machine-

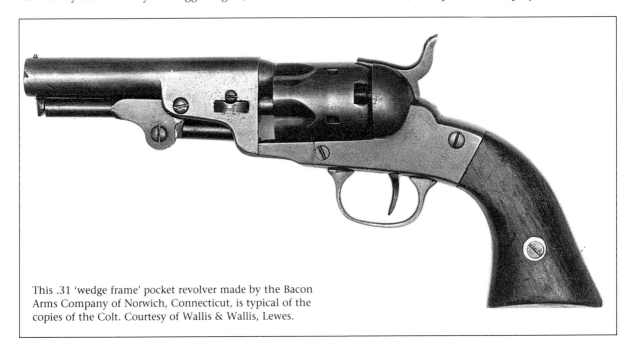

This .31 'wedge frame' pocket revolver made by the Bacon Arms Company of Norwich, Connecticut, is typical of the copies of the Colt. Courtesy of Wallis & Wallis, Lewes.

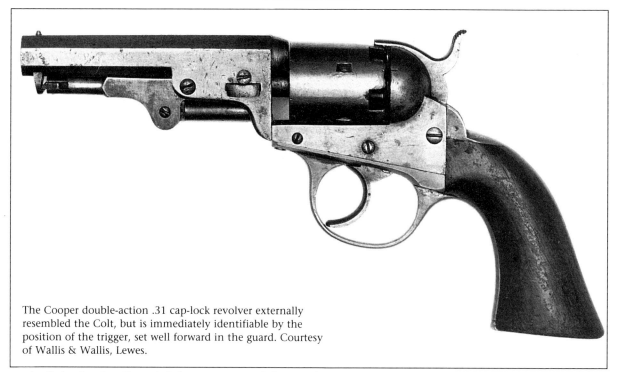

The Cooper double-action .31 cap-lock revolver externally resembled the Colt, but is immediately identifiable by the position of the trigger, set well forward in the guard. Courtesy of Wallis & Wallis, Lewes.

made Colts in the Crystal Palace was devalued by the appearance of a solid-frame self-cocking revolver on the stand of George & John Deane.

The Adams revolver was the one great success of the English handgun industry in the middle of the nineteenth century. The original gun was a five-chambered, solid-frame pattern with a self-cocking trigger mechanism and a distinctive spurless hammer. It was protected by an English Patent granted to Robert Adams in 1851 (No. 13,527), which also protected breech-loading sporting rifles. The revolver may even have been added as an afterthought; but, though it was accorded no prominence in the catalogues of the Great Exhibition of the Industry of All Nations, an 'electro-plated silver revolving pistol, ebony stock, silver studded' was to be the cornerstone of Adams's success.

The exhibition judges initially paid greater attention to the decorative submissions of gunmakers in France and Spain, before the flamboyance of Colt drew attention to the technological – not artistic –

merits of the revolver. Adams and the Deanes received a prize medal for 'double & single guns & pistols properly finished', and the era of the truly English revolver had begun.

The advent of the revolvers had not passed without interest. *The Times* reported in the summer of 1851 that Colts had been purchased by officers of the 12th Lancers, ordered to Cape Colony, and a Select Committee assembled at Woolwich in September to test the .44 six-shot Dragoon Colt against a lighter 32-bore five-shot Adams. There was little to choose between the rivals, though the Colt was clumsier and the Adams, owing to its double-action lock, could shoot faster.

By 1852 the Adams revolver was being offered in three sizes. The 38-Bore Target or Holster pattern had a 10in barrel and weighed 2lb 14oz; an intermediate 54-Bore version, weighing 2lb, had an 8in barrel; and the smallest, 120-Bore or Pocket size, with a 6in barrel, weighed a mere 18oz. Deane, Adams & Deane claimed that all parts except the hammer, the trig-

ger and the springs were being made on machinery, but true mechanisation does not seem to have been accomplished until the mid-1850s. Sales were very encouraging, and were exceeding 10,000 annually when the Crimean War began in 1854. Adams revolvers were licensed to several gunmaking companies, including William Tranter of Birmingham, J. & R. Brazier of Wolverhampton, and Auguste Francotte or Pirlot Frères in Liége. Guns may often be found with retailers' marks, such as 'Moore & Woodward' or 'E. M. Reilly & Company'.

The original self-cocking Adams revolver, though its one-piece frame was extremely sturdy, had two important disadvantages in addition to the comparative fragility of its lockwork. The absence of a hammer spur prevented thumb-cocking, and the lack of a rammer hindered loading. Seating the bullet in the chamber had to be done by thumb pressure alone, which was not always sufficient to prevent the bullets jarring forward to leave a gap ahead of the powder charge. The Colt had a powerful

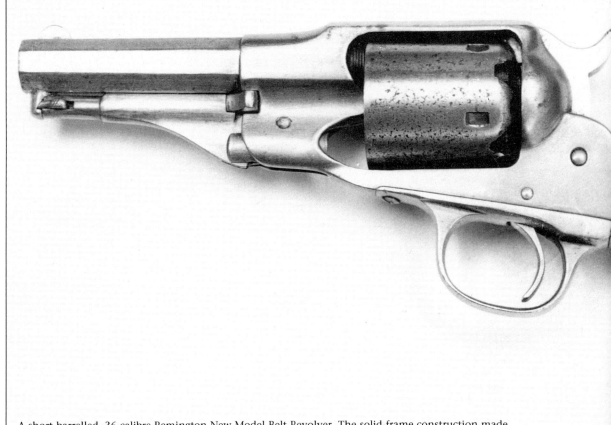

A short-barrelled .36-calibre Remington New Model Belt Revolver. The solid-frame construction made it much more durable than the open-frame Colts, though the components of the lockwork were fragile and a lack of clearance allowed cap debris to jam the cylinder. Courtesy of Ian Hogg.

pivoting rammer to seat each bullet firmly on to the powder charge. Excessive pressures were rarely generated in the American guns, which rapidly attained a reputation for excellent accuracy. Experience in the Crimea, however, showed that the .36 Colt bullet was a poor man-stopper compared with the 54-Bore (.442) Adams pattern.

Colt's London business went into a rapid and terminal decline. By this time Robert Adams had made substantial improvements to his basic design. A hesitation lock had been patented in November 1853, relying on one hard pull on the trigger lever to cock the hammer and a second light pull to release it. Comparatively few of these guns were made; though they could be shot more accurately than the standard self-cocking guns, the

advent of the Beaumont lock rendered them obsolete.

Later guns – with rammers patented in 1854–5 by John Rigby, Adams himself and James Kerr – had a modified spur-hammer lock patented in 1855 by Lieutenant Frederick Beaumont of the Royal Engineers. However, the partnership of Adams and the Deanes ceased in the summer of 1856 and production began in the Bermondsey factory of the newly-formed London Armoury Company. The Armoury initially made Beaumont-Adams revolvers in 38-, 54- and 120-Bore, though the largest was abandoned in 1859 and the smallest version is comparatively rare. The pocket revolvers generally had 4½in barrels. Except for a few of the earliest, the guns were all fitted with Kerr-patent rammers.

Substantial orders for Beaumont-Adams revolvers were placed by the War Office in October 1855, but the war in the Crimea ended before they could be completed. Guns were sent to the USA during the American Civil War through wholesalers Schuyler, Hartley & Graham of New York City, but the quantities involved were small. A licence to make the Beaumont-Adams revolver had been exploited by the Massachusetts Arms Company in the mid-1850s, but work had ceased before hostilities began.

The rivalry between Adams and Colt stimulated interest in the cap-lock revolver in Britain, not so much for military service (few British gunmakers had the production capacity), but instead to satisfy growing commercial demand.

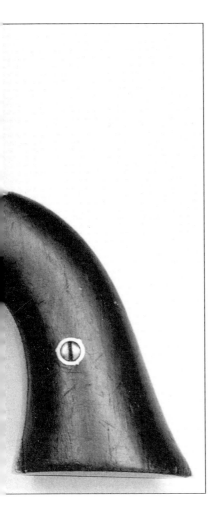

The transitional phase linking pepperboxes with true revolvers was short. Most of the transitional guns made in Britain were probably inspired by the publicity generated by Colt, particularly, during the Great Exhibition of 1851. They were made simply by shortening the archetypal pepperbox barrel cluster and adding a barrel. Indeed, there is every possibility that some original pepperboxes were changed to 'proto revolver' form in this period, though this would probably have been confined to only a few individual examples as re-proof was necessary.

The quality of the transitional firearms varied according to price, from some crudely finished guns at the bottom of the scale to high-quality products with engraved brass frames or German silver mounts. Some of the finest were accompanied by cases compartmented for accessories and lined in baize or plush.

Transitional revolvers suffered from several major drawbacks. The self-cockers usually had a knuckle-whitening trigger pull, while many guns lacked fences between the nipples and were prone to chain-firing. Others leaked gas copiously at the junction of the chamber and barrel.

Typical of the British products were guns made to a registered design granted in April 1852 to Thomas Baker of Fleet Street, London. This protected an elongated cocking lever or 'hammer tail'. If the serial numbers on surviving Baker revolvers are a reliable indicator (other types of firearm could have been included in the sequence), then more than 2,500 handguns of this particular type were made in the 1850s.

Virtually all of the cap-lock transitional revolvers, by nature of their pepperbox origins, were weakly constructed. The barrels were often attached to the cylinder axis pin and lacked the support available even in the open-frame Colt. They were greatly inferior to the sturdy, solid-framed Adams designs. Their lives would have been short had they ever seen arduous service, but the condition of most surviving examples suggests that they spent most of their time in bureaux, desk drawers, or fitted cases. The linear construction of these transitional revolvers, reflecting their pepperbox pedigree, emphasised overall length.

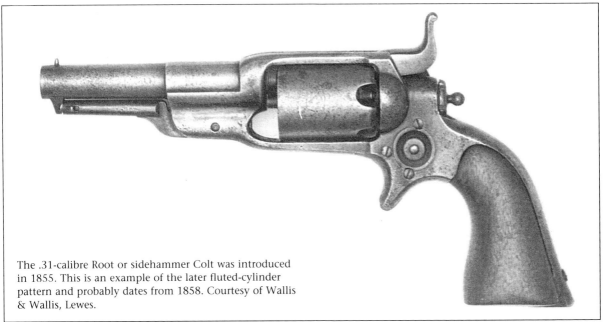

The .31-calibre Root or sidehammer Colt was introduced in 1855. This is an example of the later fluted-cylinder pattern and probably dates from 1858. Courtesy of Wallis & Wallis, Lewes.

Consequently, very few pocketable examples are found, even though their calibre may be as small as 120-Bore.

The success of the revolvers designed by Robert Adams persuaded a few English gunsmiths to abandon their transitional designs. However, the complexity of the cap-lock revolver was enough to restrict production to a handful of manufacturers. Even though many differing names are encountered, most will prove to be provincial gunsmiths who had simply bought the guns in London or Birmingham.

Revolvers patented by William Harding in 1858 were made by John Deane & Sons after the split with Robert Adams. Their distinctive features included a barrel block which hooked into the lower front of the frame and was retained by a cross-pin or latch on the back-strap of the frame ahead of the hammer. The Deane-Hardings included a few five-shot, 4½in-barrelled, 120-Bore pocket revolvers, 9½in overall and weighing about 22oz. Some 120-Bore guns were supplied in convertible form, with additional cylinders chambering .30 rimfire cartridges. These have six chambers instead of the non-convertible guns' five.

Webley made six-shot 'Longspur' revolvers in 120-Bore, with barrels of 2½–4in, and a few of the later 1857-type Wedge Frame guns in 100-Bore. Joseph Lang even made revolvers incorporating a gas-seal mechanism, achieved by pressing the cylinder forward over the barrel during the firing cycle. Most guns of this type are general-purpose size, with 60-Bore chambers and 70-Bore barrels, but a handful of 120-Bore pocket revolvers accompanied them. George Daw also made self-cocking and double-action revolvers, including a few pocketable examples.

William Tranter of Birmingham made a variety of designs, the oldest, patented in 1853, relying on a distinctive two-trigger system. These guns could either be fired as self-cockers, simply by pulling through on both triggers at once, or as hesitation-cockers by pulling back on the spur beneath the guard to cock the hammer and then pressing the lever within the guard to release it. First-pattern Tranters were made in sizes ranging from a tiny 120-Bore pocket revolver to a 38-Bore holster pattern. Second-pattern or single-trigger, double-action Tranter revolvers, patented in Britain in 1856, were also made in 120-Bore.

The popularity of the cap-lock revolver in Britain was not matched throughout Continental Europe, owing to the rapid introduction of the pinfire cartridge in the middle of the nineteenth century. This was particularly true in the pocket-revolver classes, where the advantages of metal-case cartridges carrying their own priming were obvious. No longer would it be necessary to fumble with separate balls or tiny percussion caps.

Copies of the cap-lock Colts were made in Austria, Belgium and Russia; licensed copies of the Adams were made in Belgium, by Dandoy, Francotte and Pirlot in Liége. A variant of the Beaumont-Adams was even made in Suhl for the Prussian navy, allegedly by Schmidt & Habermann, though they are clearly marked 'S & N'.

A typical 120-Bore double-action Adams-type pocket revolver of the 1850s, probably made by one of the many licensees in Liége. Courtesy of Frederick J. Wilkinson.

CARTRIDGE REVOLVERS

PINFIRE DESIGNS

The first revolvers to successfully chamber self-contained metal-case cartridges were pinfires, credit for the distinctive ammunition normally being given to Casimir Lefaucheux of Paris. Development of the cartridges began in the 1830s, but the manufacturing techniques took years to perfect, and the earliest pinfire pepperboxes were not made until 1848–9. These were followed almost immediately by the first pinfire revolvers, said to have been made for the French army by Casimir Lefaucheux's son, Eugéne. Unremarkable mechanically, they had

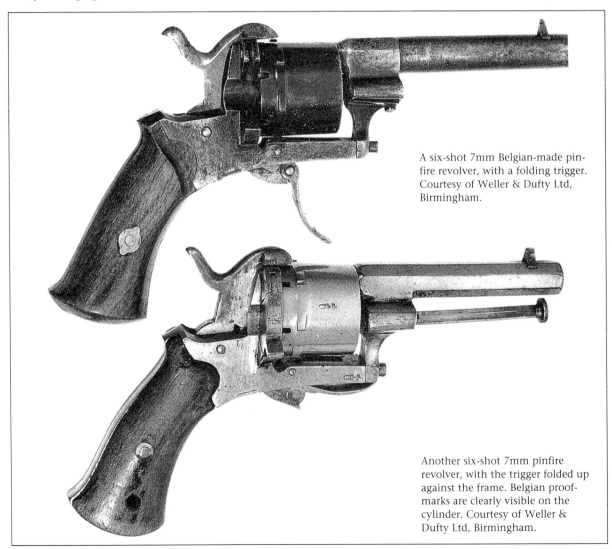

A six-shot 7mm Belgian-made pinfire revolver, with a folding trigger. Courtesy of Weller & Dufty Ltd, Birmingham.

Another six-shot 7mm pinfire revolver, with the trigger folded up against the frame. Belgian proofmarks are clearly visible on the cylinder. Courtesy of Weller & Dufty Ltd, Birmingham.

the great advantages of metal-case ammunition.

A Lefaucheux-type revolver adopted by the French navy in the autumn of 1857 had improved double-action lockwork credited to Chaineux. Acceptance in France finally assured the success of the genre, though pinfire revolvers of all types eventually became universally (if mistakenly) known as 'Lefaucheux' owing to the source of inspiration.

Pinfire revolvers were popular with gunsmiths in Austria-Hungary, Belgium, Germany and Spain. The products of individual gunmakers could sometimes be identified by their features, but, owing to widespread copying, certainty is rarely possible unless the revolvers are signed. The pinfire system became so popular in Europe that many guns shared a common design.

BETTER DESIGNS

The ever-increasing distribution of centre-fire revolvers had no immediate impact on the success of the European pinfire. Pinfire cartridges were cheaper and easier to make than centre-fire designs, so production of pinfire revolvers continued as late as 1914. Ammunition was still being made for them in the 1930s. Yet the revolvers themselves were steadily improved as centre-fire rivals gained a foothold on the European market, one of the most important changes being the supersession of open frames by stronger solid-top designs.

A rudimentary closed frame could be created simply by extending the barrel-strap back into the upper part of the breech face, where it was retained by screws, pins or latches. Guns of this type were undoubtedly sturdier than their open-frame predecessors, but remained markedly inferior to true solid-frame guns.

Pinfire revolvers were made in a variety of sizes, shapes and chamberings. They ranged from tiny 6mm-calibre pocket revolvers to a ridiculously ponderous 21-shot double-barrel gun complete with a folding bayonet. Calibre usually lay in the 7mm-12mm range, though the power of even the largest cartridge was meagre.

The classical medium-size gun of the 1870s, inspired by Lefaucheux, had an open frame. The barrel block was attached by locking the cylinder axis-pin in the breech face, and then fixing the lower part of the block to the extension of the frame beneath the cylinder. Many of the smaller pocketable guns had folding triggers which often sprang down beneath the frame when the hammer was drawn back.

A simple sliding ejector rod beneath the barrel, offset to the right, was used in conjunction with a hinged loading gate behind the cylinder on the right side of the frame to expel spent cartridge cases. The rod was usually held in place by a simple spring catch. The cylinder surface was smooth except for the locking-bolt notches. The front sight was often simply nothing but a bead-topped rod screwed into the muzzle, or could be formed integrally with the barrel. Back sights were either a small 'V'-block on the frame or a notch cut into the hammer nose. Most grips flared outward to the butt cap, which often carried a lanyard ring, and a prominent hump or 'prawl' could be found on the back strap behind the hammer.

Some European Pinfire Revolver Manufacturers

Henri Arendt, Liége, Belgium.
Manufacture d'Armes Begeuldre, Liége, Belgium.
Établissements Coquet, Liége, Belgium.
Gustave Delvigne, Paris, France.
Leopold Gasser, Ottakring, nr Vienna, Austria-Hungary.
Alessandro Guerriero, Genoa, Italy.
F. Jung & Söhne, Suhl, Saxony (Germany).
Antonin Lebeda, Prague, Austria-Hungary.
Casimir and Eugéne Lefaucheux, Paris, France.
Manufacture d'Armes Lepage, Liége, Belgium.
Manufacture Liégeoise d'Armes à Feu, Liége, Belgium.
Orbea Hermanos, Eibar, Spain.
A. Raick (later Raick Frères), Liége, Belgium.
Henri Renault (later Rolland & Renault), Liége, Belgium.
Établissements Verney-Carron, Saint-Étienne, France.
Philip Webley & Son, Birmingham, England.

The construction of pocket revolvers generally duplicated the larger versions, though calibre was usually only 5mm-7mm. However, many had folding triggers and bobbed or spurless hammers to reduce the chance of accidental discharge as the revolver was drawn from a pocket. Many lacked ejector rods, and others, made without barrels, resembled pepperboxes. Short-barrel or barrelless guns were occasionally built into cases – the Frankenau purse pistol being an example – or fitted with folding knife blades. These could be attached to the frame or pivoted beneath the barrel.

Some of the later solid-frame pinfire revolvers with sheath triggers resembled the 'Suicide Specials' popular in the USA in the last quarter of the nineteenth century. Dual-purpose convertible guns relied on movable firing pins or a special two-stage hammer to allow pin-, rim- or centre-fire cartridges to be used interchangeably.

Pin-fire pocket revolvers were very popular in Europe but almost unknown in North America, where rim- and centre-fire patterns prevailed. A catalogue published about 1866 by Philip Webley & Son illustrated a typical range of pinfire revolvers available from a single agency, ranging from a small open-frame self-cocking pepperbox to a cumbersome twelve-shot open-frame gun. Calibres were customarily 7mm, 9mm or 12mm. There is little doubt that these guns were bought in Belgium; the cylinder of the 'Webley' solid-frame pinfire revolver, for example, was locked by a combination 'L'-bolt and cylinder axis pin beneath the barrel. This had been patented *c.*1863 by Albert Fagnus of Liége.

THE FIRST RIMFIRE REVOLVERS
Although the pinfire cartridge was very popular in Europe, it was too delicate to withstand rough treatment; the exposed pin was particularly vulnerable. Consequently, guns of this type made practically no impression in North America.

A major change occurred with the introduction of rimfire ammunition, another of the many ideas that had originated in France. The earliest satisfactory design is said to have been produced by Houllier, but credit for transforming the idea into commercial reality is usually given to Flobert. Rimfire pistols were exhibited in the Great Exhibition in London in 1851, but acceptance was very slow. The situation did not change until Horace Smith and Daniel Wesson abandoned the Volition Repeater (later known as the Volcanic) to exploit a revolver patented by Rollin White, with the individual chambers bored entirely through the cylinder.

When Colt's master patent expired in 1857, Smith & Wesson unveiled a seven-shot mechanically rotated .22 rimfire revolver. Introduced commercially in January 1858, the Model No. 1 was not especially noteworthy. The method of indexing the cylinder was poor, and the absence of a safety or half-cock notch on the hammer was enough to cause occasional accidents.

The Smith & Wesson, widely regarded as a toy when it appeared, was destined to become extremely popular. Although only about 11,000 of the original 'old pattern' had been made when an improved 'second pattern' appeared in May 1860, the Model No. 1 was greatly favoured by the Federal forces during the American Civil War of 1861–5. It was regularly carried by officers and rank-and-file to supplement standard weapons. Smith & Wessons were commonly purchased by soldiers' wives and sweethearts, and were often contained in tin-plate or gutta-percha cases. The benefits of the Civil War were clearly shown when, in April 1869, the agreement concluded with Rollin White lapsed; more than 270,000 licensed revolvers had been made, earning White nearly $68,000 in royalties.

Smith & Wesson had always realised that the tiny .22 rimfire cartridge performed very poorly, but were initially handicapped by technological limitations. A load of only three grains of black powder was the most that could be contained safely in the earliest seamless copper cartridge cases, and a bullet weighing only thirty grains could not have the stopping power of the heavyweight balls fired by .36 or .44 Colts.

The worst problems had been overcome by 1861, allowing the introduction of a .32 rimfire cartridge. A load of thirteen grains of powder and a 90-grain bullet greatly improved power, though excessive fouling and corrosion still presented serious problems. Six-shot .32 Model No. 2 revolvers, made with barrels measuring 4–6in, were supplemented after 1864 by the .32 Model No. 1½. These lightweight five-shot guns originally had 3½in barrels, but a 4in pattern was substituted in 1866.

No sooner had the final Confederate surrender been accepted than Smith & Wesson began refining the design of the Nos. 1 and 1½ revolvers to correct the faults that had been shown by military service, simultaneously adding fea-

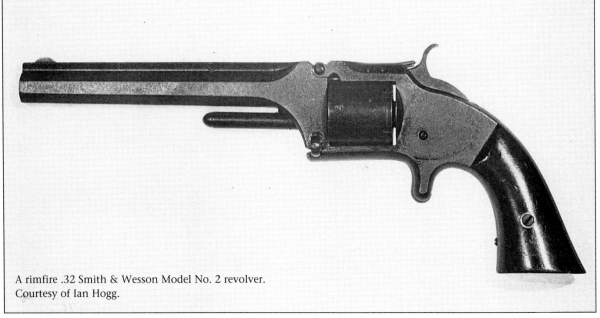

A rimfire .32 Smith & Wesson Model No. 2 revolver.
Courtesy of Ian Hogg.

tures demanded by the growing commercial market. The cylinders were fluted, cylindrical barrels were substituted for the original octagonal forms, and bird's head butts replaced the squared-heel type.

INFRINGEMENTS OF THE SMITH & WESSON REVOLVERS

Like many successful innovators, Horace Smith and Daniel Wesson were soon faced with challenges to their supremacy. Fortunately for Smith & Wesson, however, the terms of the agreement made Rollin White liable for action taken against infringers. Cases pursued through the Federal courts ate heavily into White's royalties.

Among the Smith & Wesson-type revolvers made legitimately, under the terms of the licence, were those of the Rollin White Arms Company – or, at least, its earliest incarnation. Smith & Wesson had even purchased 10,000 .22 rimfires from this particular source. White subsequently resigned after a disagreement among the partners, the original company was liquidated, and the remaining assets were purchased by the Lowell Arms Company. Production began again under new management. As Rollin White had no stake in the Lowell Arms Company, these revolvers clearly infringed Smith & Wesson's rights. The ensuing court case predictably resolved in the appellants' favour; Lowell was ordered to surrender all the guns that had been completed, 1,853 of them, and work ceased.

Smith & Wesson were formidable opponents, employing the leading lawyers of the day to pursue transgressors through the courts with great vigour. Among the first to feel the company's wrath was Herman Boker of New York, who had been selling 'bored-through cylinder' revolvers made by the Manhattan Fire Arms Company. This suit resolved in favour of Smith & Wesson and Rollin White in 1862.

Actions subsequently brought against Thomas Bacon, Daniel Moore, Lucius Pond and James Warner were all decided in favour of Smith & Wesson. However, the defendants were customarily allowed to complete guns 'in the course of manufacture', as long as appropriate royalties were paid to the assignees of the Rollin White patent. These guns were marked APRIL 3, 1855, to signify that the dues had been paid. Nearly 11,000, in chamberings ranging from .22 to .38 rimfire, were eventually purchased by Smith & Wesson for resale. The most popular were the 4,880 .32 rimfire Pond revolvers.

Smith & Wesson Infringements of the Civil War Era

Allen & Wheelock and Allen & Company, Worcester, Massachusetts
   Made centre- and side-hammer guns in rim- and lip-fire, calibres ranging from .22 to .44.
Bacon Arms & Manufacturing Company, Norwich, Connecticut
   Made a Smith & Wesson copy in .22 or .32.
Samuel Cone, West Chesterfield, Massachusetts
   Made a .32 Smith & Wesson copy.
William Irving, New York
   Made a Smith & Wesson copy (.22 or .32), and a special convertible gun.
Manhattan Fire Arms Company, Newark, New Jersey
   Made Smith & Wesson copies in .22 and .32.
Daniel Moore & Company, Brooklyn, New York
   Made patented revolvers ranging from .32 to .44.
Lucius Pond, Worcester, Massachusetts
   Made a modified Smith & Wesson in .32 and .44.
Edward Prescott, Worcester, Massachusetts
   Made a .32 Smith & Wesson copy and a modified gun with a special cylinder latch.
James Warner, Springfield, Massachusetts

Made a .30 rimfire derivative of Warner's cap-lock pocket revolver.

Many defendants claimed that their guns were made in accordance with patents other than Rollin White's, hoping, often against hope, to influence the decisions of the courts. Thomas Bacon averred that his revolvers embodied a swinging cylinder patented in May 1862 by Charles Hopkins; William Irving contended that his convertible rimfire/cap-lock revolvers were being made in accordance with a patent granted in April 1863 to James Reid; and the distinctive revolvers being made in Brooklyn by Daniel Moore had a pivoting frame/cylinder assembly, patented in September 1860, which could be turned laterally to the right to reload. Lucius Pond was making guns incorporating a patent granted to Abram Gibson in July 1860, whilst Edwin Prescott was using a cylinder latch patented in October 1860. Unfortunately, none of these claims was enough to invalidate the original Rollin White patent of 1855, even though some of the guns were undoubtedly improvements on the primitive Smith & Wesson Model No. 1.

Interestingly, Elliot, Rupertus and Sharps made pepperboxes with bored-through cylinders, all of which could be classed as infringements, yet there is no evidence that Smith & Wesson ever took action against them.

Unlicensed copies of the Smith & Wesson revolvers were also made in Europe. Many clearly have English parentage, but their origins are obscure. Even though W. C. Scott of Birmingham and Joseph Lang of London have been identified with them, there is little doubt that these particular gunsmiths were acting as retailers. Suggestions have been made that most of the English guns were made by Philip Webley & Son, but the evidence is unconvincing. Proof marks suggest that the Continental examples were generally made in Liége,

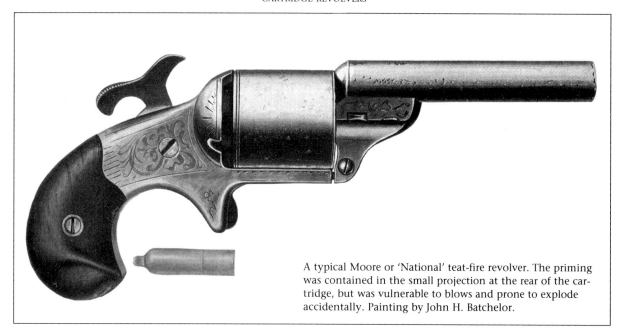

A typical Moore or 'National' teat-fire revolver. The priming was contained in the small projection at the rear of the cartridge, but was vulnerable to blows and prone to explode accidentally. Painting by John H. Batchelor.

though a few large military-style guns were made in Suhl in the 1870s for the Saxon army.

EVASIONS OF THE SMITH & WESSON REVOLVERS

The gunmaking industry in New England, which had previously been challenged to make revolvers which did not infringe the Colt cylinder-rotation patent, was now faced with an equally effective restriction on bored-through cylinders. Smith & Wesson so quickly showed a willingness to sue potential transgressors that the only way of competing would clearly involve something completely different.

The attempts to evade the Rollin White patent were much more interesting than the simple copies of the Smith & Wesson Model No. 1. Considered as a group, they are among the most fascinating of all nineteenth-century firearms, and show how far ingenuity could be stretched in pursuit of commercial gain.

One of the most enterprising designs was patented in 1859–63 by Willard Ellis and John White, and licensed to Plant's Manufacturing Company of Southington, Connecticut. This particular gunmaking business had a peripatetic

existence, moving from Southington to nearby New Haven in 1861, then to Plantsville in 1866 before briefly returning to Southington in the late 1860s.

The Ellis & White revolver fired a metal-case 'cup primer' cartridge inserted from the front of the cylinder. Contained in an extension of the cartridge case instead of a projecting rim, the priming was struck when the nose of the hammer entered a small hole bored in the rear of the chamber.

The earliest .42 Plant revolvers resembled the Smith & Wesson Model No. 1 externally, but had nickel-plated bronze frames and blued octagonal barrels. As the Civil War intensified, growing demand for weapons of virtually any size and any type was reflected in the sales of Plant revolvers, which were surprisingly successful even though the curious ammunition was difficult to obtain outside the major centres of population.

By 1863, the hinged-frame Plant had been replaced by a stronger .28, .30 or .42 solid-frame design which lasted into the late 1860s. Most of the guns made after 1864 had an ejector patented by Henry Reynolds of Springfield, Massachusetts, and a few convertible

cap-lock/cartridge examples had exchangeable cylinders. Plant revolvers bore a wide range of markings, applied by the Eagle Arms Company of New York; John Marlin & Company of Rock Falls, New York; the Merwin & Bray Fire Arms Company of New York; and Reynolds, Plant & Hotchkiss of New Haven in Connecticut.

Cup-primer cartridges were also chambered in revolvers briefly made by the Connecticut Arms Company of Norfolk, Connecticut, soon after the end of the Civil War. Based on patents granted in 1864–6 to Stephen Wood, these .28-calibre single-action, sheath-trigger guns resembled the Smith & Wessons. However, their frames were usually brass and a spur-type extractor was set in the bottom strap.

When his seven-shot rimfire revolver was judged to infringe the Rollin White patent, Daniel Moore substituted a gun chambering a teat-fire cartridge patented in January 1864 by David Williamson. Revolvers of this type will also be found with the marks of the National Arms Company of Brooklyn, which purchased the assets of Moore's gunmaking business in the mid-1860s. Daniel Moore deserves greater credit for his designing exploits than he is customarily accorded, though his revolvers were briefly glorified when the memoirs of Major G. W. Manderson were published as *The Twin Seven Shooters*. Moore had been granted a patent in 1863 to protect a .32 teat-fire revolver with a hinged loading gate ahead of the cylinder, but had failed to claim novelty either in teat-fire or the insertion of cartridges backward from the chamber-mouth. Consequently, Moore was forced to pay royalties to Williamson when an essentially similar cartridge system was required to compete with Smith & Wesson.

Most .32 teat-fire Moore revolvers had six-chambered cylinders, open-top frames, sheath triggers, and bird's head butts. The cartridge retainer/extractor mechanism on the right side of the frame beneath the cylinder had been patented by Williamson in the summer of 1864.

Experience soon showed that teat-fire revolvers had a potentially fatal drawback. Accumulation of fouling in the chamber made cartridges difficult to seat without using force, but the teat could be crushed if too much force was applied. Accidents soon consigned the teat-fire cartridge to history.

Much more successful than the Moore teat-fire was the gun patented in 1863 by Frank Slocum, rights being assigned to the Brooklyn Firearms Company. These single-action, five-shot .32 revolvers chambered standard rimfire ammunition, evading the Rollin White patent by using detachable sliding tubular 'sleeves' in each chamber. A cartridge could be inserted in each sleeve, which was pushed forward to accept it. The sleeve was then returned to its original position. When each chamber was rotated in front of the hammer, to be struck through a slot by the hammer nose, the sleeves bore against the frame to provide support for the cartridge.

The .32-calibre revolver patented in October 1865 by Silas Crispin, made in New York by the Smith Arms Company, was another hinged-frame design. A distinctive two-part cylinder evaded the Rollin White patent. Each part of the cylinder could revolve independently until special cartridges with an annular priming-band around the case were loaded backwards through the front section of the cylinder. A striker acting downward between the two cylinders fired the unique cartridges, but the gun was never more than a limited success. The Crispin cartridge, like the European pinfire, was prone to ignite when struck accidentally.

Lucius Pond based his sheath trigger 'evasion revolver' on a patent granted in June 1862 to John Vickers. This also relied on lining tubes or 'thimbles' containing standard rimfire cartridges, which were inserted in each chamber from the front. Pond revolvers usually had brass frames and blued steel barrels. Their cylinders held seven .22 or five .32 cartridges. The cylinder axis pins of guns made after 1865 carried a pivoting 'discharger', which supposedly expelled spent cases when the chamber-thimbles were withdrawn. This system was patented in November 1864 by Freeman Hood.

European evasions were uncommon, though the Belgian-made Polain revolver, patented in the early 1860s, combined a cartridge loading system with a pierced disc to which chamber-tubes were secured. This enabled all the tubes to be inserted simultaneously.

IMPROVED SINGLE-ACTION REVOLVER DESIGNS

The first cartridge revolvers, American rimfire and European pinfire alike, were inferior to cap-locks honed to near-perfection by years of experience. The earliest Smith & Wessons were structurally weak, while few of the evasions had much to offer except unnecessary complexity. The best of the cap-lock revolvers were much more powerful than the rimfires, and solid-frame designs such as the Remington had established a reputation for durability. In Europe, particularly in England, the double-action trigger system exemplified by the Beaumont-Adams was gaining widespread approval.

The one great advantage of the cartridge revolvers lay in the ease of reloading, an area in which no cap-lock could hope to compete. Once manufacturing techniques had been perfected, the metal-case cartridge also offered greater certainty of ignition than cap, powder and ball. By 1870, therefore, the days of the cap-lock revolver were clearly drawing to a close, even though some guns lasted into the twentieth century in remote parts of the American frontier.

The two areas in which the earliest cartridge revolvers most needed improving were strength of construction and ease of loading. But these were not necessarily always compatible.

Faster loading

This became possible when the first top-break Smith & Wesson revolver was made in 1868. The cylinder and barrel assembly was latched by a sturdy bolt ahead of the hammer, and a rack mechanism contained in the hollow cylinder axis pin automatically operated a star-plate extractor when the breech was opened far enough. Testing showed that this gun had great potential, but Smith & Wesson, anxious to avoid costly litigation, wisely acquired the rights to a selection of patents granted in 1860–5 to William Dodge, Abram Gibson and Louis Rodier. Gibson's patent was particularly interesting, as it had protected the design of a 'cylinder and barrel swinging away from the recoil shield' as early as July 1860.

Armed with patents granted in the USA, Britain and elsewhere in 1869, Smith & Wesson made the first New Model No. 3 revolvers in 1870. They were the first of their type to encounter tangible success, and the ordering in May 1871 of

20,000 modified guns for the Russian army set the seal on success. By the time the last orders were placed with Smith & Wesson, in 1877, more than 160,000 revolvers had been supplied to the Tsarist army. Large numbers were subsequently made in Germany and Russia.

The success of the military-style top-break design persuaded Smith & Wesson to adapt a Model No. 1½ in 1870, but this attempt to make a pocketable top-break design was a failure. Work began again in 1874, on the basis of the highly successful Russian-type army revolver, resulting in the .38 centre-fire Single Action or 'Baby Russian'. The rack-pattern extractor was retained, but a sheathed trigger replaced the conventional bow-type guard. The first .38 guns, with barrels measuring 3½in and 4in, were shipped to wholesalers early in 1876. A 5in barrel option was added in 1877.

By the end of 1876 nearly 13,000 .38-calibre break-open guns had been made, more than 9,000 being nickelled instead of blued.

The grips were moulded gutta-percha. About 25,550 guns had been made when work ceased in favour of the improved or 'New Model' in the summer of 1877.

The rapid rise of 'Suicide Specials' (q.v.) forced Smith & Wesson to simplify the .38 Single Action in 1877 in a bid to reduce manufacturing costs. A new extractor mechanism was patented in February 1877 by Daniel Wesson and James Bullard. Production of the .38 New (or Second) Model Single Action began immediately, the first guns being assembled in July 1877; more than 108,000 had been made when the second pattern .38 was superseded by the third type in 1891. The only major change had been the introduction in 1881 of a sliding-bar-type extractor-cam actuator. Most guns were nickel-plated and had chequered gutta-percha grips.

The third .38 Single Action Smith & Wesson, the Model 1891 or 'New New Model', reverted to a conventional trigger guard. Barrel lengths ranged from 3½in to 6in, finish was blue or more popularly

nickel, and the grips were moulded from gutta-percha. Growing enthusiasm for double-action guns restricted sales, and only 28,107 third-pattern .38 Single Action revolvers had been made when work ceased in 1911.

The success of the .38 Single Action encouraged Smith & Wesson to develop a comparable .32 revolver. The first guns, embodying a rebounding hammer patented in December 1877 by Wesson and Bullard, were completed at the beginning of 1878. The barrels of the .32 Single Action ranged from 3in to 10in, but the longest versions were rarely used. When production ceased, in 1892, nearly 100,000 revolvers had been made; nine out of every ten had been plated with nickel, blued versions being notably scarce.

The Smith & Wesson top-break system was extensively copied in Europe prior to 1914. Although substantial quantities of S&W-type revolvers were made in Liége, there is no doubting that the major production centre was the Spanish town of Eibar. Before the emer-

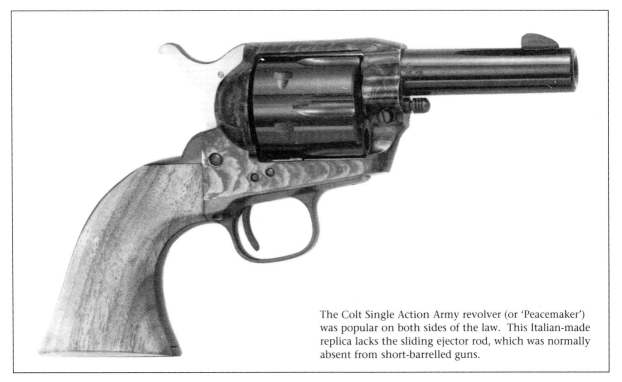

The Colt Single Action Army revolver (or 'Peacemaker') was popular on both sides of the law. This Italian-made replica lacks the sliding ejector rod, which was normally absent from short-barrelled guns.

gence of the 6.35mm-calibre FN-Browning pocket pistol, the Smith & Wesson revolvers provided the backbone of the Spanish gunmaking industry. However, though a few small single-action guns were made, most of the guns had double-action trigger systems and are considered in greater detail in the relevant chapter.

Stronger frames

Whatever the technical merits of the break-open Smith & Wessons may have been, the most popular large-calibre revolver available in the USA in the 1870s was the Colt Single Action Army model of 1873. Now better known as the 'Peacemaker', the Colt was developed as a military weapon and gained in simplicity what it undoubtedly lacked in sophistication. It can be seen, perhaps uncharitably, as a combination of the .44 cap-lock Army Colt of 1860 with the solid frame of the Civil War-era Remington and a centre-fire metallic cartridge.

Cartridges were still inserted singly though a hinged gate on the right side of the frame behind the cylinder, and spent cases were punched out by a spring-loaded ejector rod in a tubular case alongside the barrel. Even though the fixed firing pin and the absence of an efficient rebound slide prevented the Peacemaker being carried safely with the hammer down on a loaded chamber, extreme simplicity was the Colt's greatest strength. If the hammer spring broke, the gun could be fired by striking the hammer with a stone. If the cylinder pawl broke, the cylinder could still usually be turned by hand. The frame was extremely strong, with integrally forged grip straps, and the sights were robust.

The Colt Single Action Army revolver was revered on the American Frontier, where complicated designs were viewed with justifiable suspicion. Towns worthy of the name were few and far between, and a lack of experienced gunsmiths restricted the availability of repair facilities. Guns which

were lauded in the eastern USA for their mechanical sophistication were rarely as suited to the hardships of the West as their ultra-simple rivals. This view was shared by the US Army, where the .45 Colt was retained at the expense of auto-ejectors submitted by Smith & Wesson and Merwin & Hulbert.

The single-action .45 Colt remains an enduring symbol of the Wild West. Even though it was never distributed as widely as celluloid and dime novels suggest – production in 1873–1940 totalled only about 310,000 – the strength of its image has inspired a legion of modern copies. Army-type Colts were too large to serve as secret handguns. However, short-barrel conversions of cap-locks and cartridge guns alike were popular before 1900.

Low standards of workmanship suggest that most were converted locally, but even Colt's Patent Fire Arms Manufacturing Company supplied guns to special order. The short-barrel revolvers lacked ejector-rod cases and were popularly known as "Barkeep's Guns"; they were usually concealed beneath a bar counter, muzzle downward in a glass so that the hand fell easily on to the butt when required.

Among notorious short-barrel guns was a .44 Richards-Mason conversion of an 1860-pattern cap-lock, with the barrel cut immediately ahead of the flared ejector housing. This was used by one-time lawman Dallas Stoudenmire before he was killed in El Paso in 1882. A .44-40 Single Action Army Colt taken in 1894 from the corpse of Bass Outlaw had its barrel cut to 3in and lacked an ejector-rod case. Removal of the trigger allowed the hammer to be 'fanned' with the palm of the non-firing hand, the slot for the trigger in the underside of the frame being filled with spelter and the trigger guard reduced to a short spur.

The Suicide Specials

The perfection of small-calibre revolvers by Smith & Wesson

encouraged many small companies to compete, particularly in the New England states. With the exception of gunmakers who subsequently rose to prominence, most of the manufacturers made 'Suicide Specials'. This term was applied in 1948 by Duncan McConnell, writing in the *American Rifleman*, to define distinctive single-action revolvers made by as many as 50 gunmakers, not all of whom could be bothered to sign their wares. Poor manufacturing quality and strange-sounding names suggest that this anonymity was well chosen.

Revolvers of this class began to appear as soon as the Rollin White patent expired in the spring of 1869, though volume production did not commence until the early 1870s. A typical Suicide Special was a seven-shot .22 or five-shot .32, usually chambering rimfire ammunition. The frame was usually a one-piece forging (or occasionally a casting), with a detachable plate on the left side giving access to the simple single-action lockwork. Sheath triggers were customary, butts were squared or bird's heads, and the barrels measured 3in or less. The cylinders were loaded through a hinged gate on the right side of the frame, but could be removed simply by detaching the axis pin. The guns were blued or nickel plated, and often had poor-quality 'engraving' rolled into the surface of the cylinder. Grips were usually wood or gutta-percha, though mother-of-pearl was sometimes used on the gaudier nickelled guns.

Guns of this genre were made in very large numbers, particularly in the 1880s. Production is believed to have exceeded half a million annually by 1885, but then went into a steady decline; and few were being made by 1900. This was due partly to saturation of the market, but also to the emergence of better double-action revolvers. The term 'Suicide Special' is sometimes extended to include inexpensive break-open auto-ejectors, but such usage should be discouraged.

Few Suicide Specials have much claim to novelty, though, particularly among the post-1880 group, variety is encountered in barrel-locking systems, ejectors and lock work.

Among the leading manufacturers of these essentially simple single-action revolvers was Hopkins & Allen, founded in 1868, which has been linked with more than a hundred different brand names ranging from 'Acme' to 'You Bet.' Hopkins & Allen company also made revolvers for sporting-goods dealers Merwin, Hulbert & Company (later Hulbert Brothers & Company) of New York City until the business failed in 1896.

Some of the smaller revolvers introduced by Colt in the 1870s (particularly the open-frame .22 rimfire pattern) are often unfairly included in the Suicide Special group. The .41 rimfire four-shot Patent House Pistol was the first Colt to be specifically designed for metal-case ammunition. This curi-

ous-looking design, colloquially known as the 'Cloverleaf' owing to the shape of its cylinder, was offered with barrels measuring 1½in or 3in. The counter-bored chambers, patented by Charles Richards in September 1871, enveloped the case rims to provide additional security; the earliest rimfire cartridges had a reputation for bursting.

The ejector rod was contained within the cylinder axis pin, and an extra safety element was provided by turning the cylinder through 45° so that the nose of the firing pin entered a small hole cut between the chambers. Bronze frames were often plated with silver or nickel, and a sheath trigger was fitted. The original high-spur hammer was replaced by a lower pattern in 1874.

The frame of the Cloverleaf was so narrow that a detachable side plate on the left side of the gun, allied with a lug on a collar held in the frame by the cylinder pin, was

needed to prevent cartridges falling out of the side chambers when the gun was fired. The last Cloverleaf-type Colts had conventional five-shot cylinders, but lacked ejector rods.

The .22 Open-Top and .41 Cloverleaf revolvers were replaced after 1873 by 'Colt's New Breech-Loading Revolvers', subsequently advertised as the 'New Line'. Five variants – .22, .30, .32, .38 and .41 – differed only in chambering and frame size, though guns made after 1875 incorporated a cylinder-locking bolt and loading gate patented in September 1874 by William Mason. The locking-bolt slots were moved to the rear face of the cylinder in 1876. The .22 and .30 versions were only available in rimfire chamberings, but the larger guns could be supplied to order in rim- or centre-fire. New Line guns had solid frames, sheath triggers and bird's head butts. Frames were iron, with the exception of the bronze

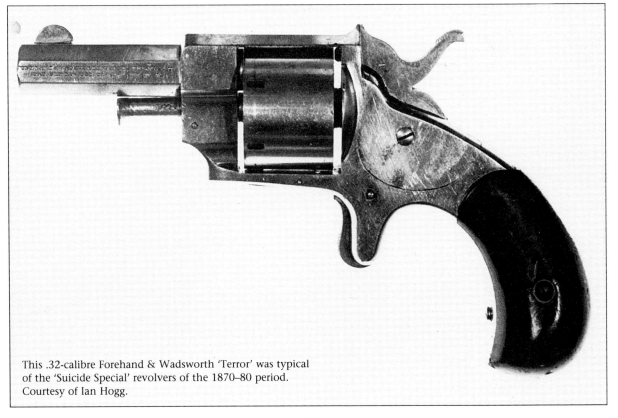

This .32-calibre Forehand & Wadsworth 'Terror' was typical of the 'Suicide Special' revolvers of the 1870–80 period. Courtesy of Ian Hogg.

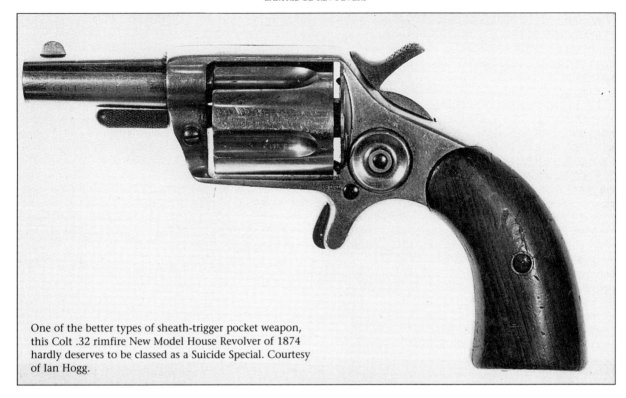

One of the better types of sheath-trigger pocket weapon, this Colt .32 rimfire New Model House Revolver of 1874 hardly deserves to be classed as a Suicide Special. Courtesy of Ian Hogg.

.22 version. Five-chamber cylinders were customary on all but the seven-shot .22. Ejectors were omitted; barrels usually measured 2½in; whilst grips could be rosewood, walnut, gutta-percha, ivory or mother-of-pearl.

Remington introduced its own New Line cartridge revolvers to compete with the Suicide Specials. Incorporating a single-action trigger and a cylinder-locking system patented in October 1873 by William Smoot, they had solid frames, sheath triggers and bird's head butts.

The five-shot Remington New Line No. 1 of 1873 chambered .30 Short rimfire cartridges. Its 2¾in octagonal barrel had an ejector rod on the right side of the frame web. The New Line No. 2 was identical with No. 1 but chambered .32 Short rimfire cartridges; No. 3, introduced in 1875, resembled its predecessors but fired .38 Short rimfires. It had a 3½in octagonal barrel and weighed 15oz.

The 1877-vintage New Line No. 4 Remington handled .38 Short

centre-fire ammunition and had a 2½in round barrel. It was the only revolver in the series to lack an ejector rod, relying instead on the cylinder axis pin to punch spent cases out of the detached cylinder. The seven-shot .22 rimfire Iroquois was similar to the No. 4 but weighed only 7¼oz, and was very slender.

About 100,000 Smoot-type revolvers were made from 1873 until the demise of E. Remington & Sons in 1886. More than half were rimfire Iroquois.

US Makers of Single-action Pocket Revolvers

NOTE: wholesalers', distributors' or spurious manufacturers' marks will often be found on Suicide Specials. Typical of these are 'Aetna Arms Co.' (Harrington & Richardson), 'Chicago Arms Co.', 'Enterprise Gun Works' (Philadelphia), 'Great Western Gun Works' (J. H. Johnson of Pittsburgh), 'Mohawk Mfg. Co. (Otis Smith), 'New York Pistol Co.', 'United States Arms Co.' and the 'Western Arms Co.'. As whole-

salers often ordered guns from more than one manufacturer simultaneously, several types of gun may bear the same brand name even though construction differs. Successful names were so often simply copied that interpretation is still sometimes disputed; there are said to be more than 30 differing revolvers marked 'Defender', made by a dozen agencies.

Bacon Manufacturing Company, Norwich, Connecticut
Bacon, Bonanza, Conqueror, Daisy, Dead Shot, Express, Gem, Governor, Guardian, Little Giant, Parole, Prairie King, Reliable, Rip Rap, U.S. Arms Co.
Colt's Patent Fire Arms Manufacturing Company, Hartford, Connecticut
New House, New Line, New Police.
Crescent Arms Company, Norwich, Connecticut
Blue Jacket, Bulldozer, Crescent, Elgin Arms, Excelsior, Faultless, Gypsy, Hartford Arms, Hibbard, Howard Arms, Knock-About,

Metropolitan, Mohawk, New York Arms, Tiger, U.S. Pistol Co., Winfield Arms Co.

E. L. Dickinson, Springfield, Massachusetts

Earl Hood, Earthquake, Our Jake, Ranger, Sterling, Toledo Firearms Co.

Ely & Wray, Springfield, Massachusetts

American, Bang-Up, Bloodhound, Panther, Tiger.

Forehand & Wadsworth Arms Company, Worcester, Massachusetts

British Bull Dog, Bulldog, Bulldozer, Electric, Pioneer, Russian Model, Swamp Angel, Terror, Wide Awake.

Harrington & Richardson Arms Company, Worcester, Massachusetts

Aetna, American, Bang-Up, Bloodhound, Crown, Eagle Arms Co., Eureka, Great Western, 'H&R', Leader, Smoky City, Victor, White Star.

Hood Firearms Company, Norwich, Connecticut

Alaska, Alert, Alexia, Alexis, Boy's Choice, Brutus, Centennial, Chichester, Continental, Czar, Hard Pan, International, Jewel, Liberty, Peerless, Princess, Rob Roy, Scout, Union Jack, 'T. & R.', Trojan, U.S. Arms Co., U.S. Pistol Co., Victoria, Whistler, Wide-Awake.

Hopkins & Allen Arms Company, Norwich, Connecticut

Acme, Alex, Allen, American Eagle, Americus, Aristocrat, Automatic, Avenger, Black & Owen, Blue Jacket, Blue Whistler, British Bulldog, Buckeye, Capt. Jack, Chichester, Creedmore, Czar, Despatch, Diamond Arms, Dictator, Double-Header, Dreadnought, Duchess, Duke, Elector, Encore, Expert, Faultless, Garrison, Governor, Half-Breed, Hinsdale, Imperial, Joker, King Pin, Leader, Life Long, Little Pet, Little Scott, Metropolitan Police, Monarch, Mountain Eagle, My Companion, Nero, Non-XL, Never Miss, Old Hickory, Oliver, Orient, Paragon, Pathfinder, Pet, Petrel, Phoenix, Ranger, Red

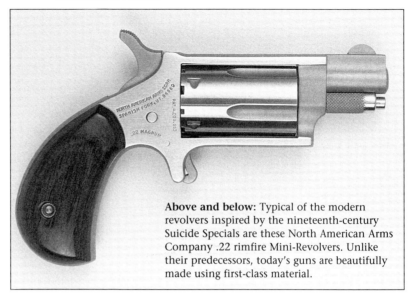

Above and below: Typical of the modern revolvers inspired by the nineteenth-century Suicide Specials are these North American Arms Company .22 rimfire Mini-Revolvers. Unlike their predecessors, today's guns are beautifully made using first-class material.

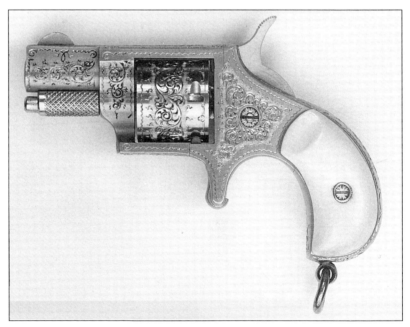

Hot, Reliable, Reliance, Royal, Scott, Spitfire, Striker, Thames Arms Co., 'T. & R.', Toledo Arms Co., Tower's Safety Police, Union, Western Bulldog, White Jacket, Wonder, 'XL', X-Pert, You Bet

Johnson, Bye & Company and Iver Johnson, Worcester and Fitchburg, Massachusetts

Bengal, Blue Jacket, Buffalo Bill, Bull Dozer, Challenger, Champion, Defender, Eagle, Eclipse, Encore, Eureka, Favorite, Favorite Navy, Hard Pan, Hecla, Invincible, Kentucky, Lion, Manhattan, Monarch, Old Hickory, Red Hot, Smoker, Southron, Tiger, Tramps Terror, Tycoon.

Lee Arms Company, Wilkes-Barre, Pennsylvania

Imperial, Red Jacket, Royal, Wm. Tell.

Marlin Fire Arms Company, New Haven, Connecticut

Joker, 'O.K.', XXX Standard.

Maltby, Curtiss & Company and Maltby, Henley & Company

Metropolitan Police.

Meriden Arms Company, Meriden, Connecticut

Aubrey, Meriden, Senator, Standard.

Norwich Arms Company and Norwich Falls Pistol Company, Norwich, Connecticut

Bulldozer, Champion, Commanche, Defiance, Frontier.

Prescott Pistol Company, Hatfield, Connecticut

Comet, Hornet, Paragon, Star.

E. Remington & Sons, Ilion, New York State

Iroquois, New Line.

Rome Revolver & Novelty Works, Rome, New York State

Mohawk, Northfield Knife Co., Rome.

J. Rupertus Patent Pistol Manufacturing Company, Philadelphia, Pennsylvania

Empire, General, Hero, Nero, Protector Arms Co., Ranger, Riker, Terrier.

Ryan Pistol Company, Norwich, Connecticut

'A.A.Co.', Cheever & Burchard, Hecla, Marquis of Lorne, Napoleon, Premier, Premium, Red Cloud, Retriever, Sitting Bull, Sport.

C. S. Shatuck, Hatfield, Massachusetts

Boom, Commercial, Unique.

Otis Smith, Middlefield and Rock Fall, Connecticut

Bull's Eye, Cadet, Liberty, Lone Star, Mohawk Arms Co., Mohegan, Odd Fellow, Royal.

William Uhlinger, Philadelphia, Pennsylvania

Grant

Wesson & Harrington, Worcester, Massachusetts

Whitney Arms Company, Whitneyville, Connecticut

Eagle, Monitor, Union Arms Co., Whitneyville Armory.

Some of these guns were made in vast numbers. By 1908 three million revolvers bearing the Harrington & Richardson trademarks alone had been made. They were also cheap: standard Johnson, Bye & Company Old Hickory guns cost

$35–60 *per dozen* in 1881, when the Forehand & Wadsworth Bulldog retailed for just $4.75.

DOUBLE-ACTION REVOLVERS

The emergence of efficient double-action cartridge revolvers ultimately had an important effect on the development of personal-defence weapons, even though the principle of double-action was scarcely new. Colt had had a running battle with the English-made Adams cap-lock in the 1850s; the double-action .36 or navy-calibre revolver promoted by Ebenezer Starr had been purchased in quantity during the American Civil War; and J. M. Cooper of Philadelphia had patented an efficient pocket- revolver design in the early 1860s. However, though several lesser manufacturers in New England had reintroduced double-action in the mid 1870s, Colt and Smith & Wesson clung for many years to conventional single-action designs.

Solid-frame guns

Although most of the cap-lock Colts and Lefaucheux-type pinfires had open-top frames, the solid-frame revolver also had a lengthy pedigree. The British Adams, the Starrs and the Remingtons (both American) were among the best known.

The advent of powerful self-contained metal-case cartridges favoured the European solid-frame revolver, which could handle increased chamber pressures in greater safety. One of the first guns of this type was made by Philip Webley & Son of Birmingham for the Royal Irish Constabulary (RIC). Unwilling to issue single-shot or even multi-chamber cap-locks, the constabulary, formed in January 1868, selected a compact short-barrel solid frame .442 Webley. The revolver had a double-action trigger system, somewhat similar to that of earlier Tranters, and a plain cylinder which rotated clockwise. The locking bolt notches lay at the front of the cylinder surface.

A rod carried in a pivoting collar was used to push spent cases backwards through the hinged loading gate on the right side of the frame, behind the cylinder. An ejector of this type was patented in July 1872 by John Adams, but Webley had been using it in a primitive form for some time. However, an Adams-pattern ejector rod was fitted to the No. 1 New Model Webley from 1879.

The RIC No. 1 revolver was a compact gun, measuring merely 9in overall with a 4in barrel; its unladen weight was about 30oz. Guns of this general type soon became popular for colonial service, particularly in the Australian states and southern Africa. Offered in several chamberings in the .44-.476 group, the No. 1 RIC revolver was also very appealing commercially, owing to a combination of good quality, robust design, small size and large calibre. Guns are found with nickel or silver plating, often engraved or highly decorated, and may have barrels as short as 2in.

The No. 2 Webley, with a prawled butt and an improved cylinder-bolting system, was offered in .320, .380 or .442; the smallest five-shot guns had 2⅛in barrels, were 5⅞in overall, and weighed a mere 12½oz. The otherwise similar No. 3 lacked an ejector, relying instead on the detachable cylinder axis pin.

The Model 83 (offered in .450 and .455) had a fluted five-chamber cylinder and an Adams-type ejector-rod collar. It was about 7in long, had a 2½in barrel, weighed 18-20oz, and was still being advertised in Webley & Scott catalogues as late as 1939.

The Webley Metropolitan Police ('MP'), a short-barrelled .450 derivative of the RIC No. 1, was 7in overall, had a 2½in barrel, weighed 27oz and had a six-chamber cylinder and a pivoting collar-type ejector rod housed in the cylinder axis pin. It also had a lanyard ring on the butt. The first purchases were made in the autumn of 1883, the sturdy and efficient weapons serving until replaced after 1911 by a .32 Webley & Scott autoloader.

The success of these powerful short-barrel handguns inspired Webley to make ultra-compact versions solely for commercial sale. The No. 2 Bull Dog of 1879, often marked THE BRITISH BULL DOG, remained in the company's catalogues until the beginning of the First World War. This five-shot revolver could be obtained in three chamberings: .320, .380 or .450. Weight ranged from 11oz to 18oz, and overall length varied from 5⅞in to 6⅓in. Short bird's-head grips were standard, though occasional variations were made in small quantities – e.g., the 'Ulster Bull Dog' had a long grip, and the frame of the 'Tower Bull Dog' extended backwards to give a prawled back-strap not unlike that of the Colt Lightning. Bull Dog-type revolvers were exceptionally successful in European markets, where they proved a revela-

tion to purchasers used to weak pinfires of broadly comparable dimensions.

Most of the copies made in Belgium or Spain differed greatly in detail from their English prototypes, yet clearly derived from the same lineage. Some were even made in the USA, chiefly by Forehand & Wadsworth. Markings might include BULL DOG, BRITISH BULL DOG, BULFIGHTER (sic), BELGIAN BULL DOG or a selection of proprietary variations. Many bear the markings of Francotte of Liége (a crowned 'AF'); Charles Ph. Clément of Liége; Henrion, Dassy & Heuschen ('HDH') of Liége; Manufacture Liégeoise d'Armes à Feu ('ML'); or Rongé fils. Chamberings from 6.35mm to .450 may be encountered. Safety catches are common on Belgian products, though the degree of sophistication varies: the .320 Francotte 'Mylady' had a slider on the frame immediately above the trigger-

back, while rival designs may have radial levers or even a simple sliding plate behind the hammer.

The European-made 'Constabulary' or 'Police' revolvers were broadly similar to the Webley RIC patterns but were available in chamberings including 7.62mm Nagant, 8mm Lebel, .320, 9.4mm Dutch, .380, .44 and .450. Many attempts have been made to classify them, not always successfully. Suffice it to say that the guns differ greatly in style, size, construction and detail. They sold far and very wide: a pair of Webley RIC-type revolvers was carried by Colonel George A. Custer at the Battle of the Little Big Horn, and a .38-calibre British Bulldog, maker unknown, was taken from the waistcoat pocket of outlaw Bob Dalton after the disastrous assault of the Dalton Gang on the banks in the Kansas town of Coffeyville in 1892.

Double-action solid-frame pocket revolvers were also very popular

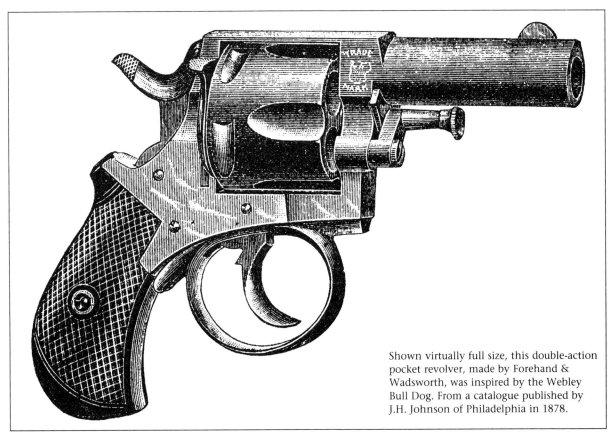

Shown virtually full size, this double-action pocket revolver, made by Forehand & Wadsworth, was inspired by the Webley Bull Dog. From a catalogue published by J.H. Johnson of Philadelphia in 1878.

in Europe, ranging from the 'Pocket Bull Dogs' (which were usually little more than diminutives of the full-size Bull Dog) to the minuscule 'Puppy' series. The simplest guns were loaded by detaching the cylinders, whereas more sophisticated examples had pivoting-collar rod ejectors. Some had folding or ring triggers, others had enclosed or spurless hammers, and a few had radial-lever safety catches on the side of the frame. The diversity of construction was matched only by the gunsmiths who made them. Many twentieth-century products were styled on semi-automatic pistols, capitalising on the great suc-

cess of the 6.35mm FN-Brownings and .25 Colts prior to 1914.

Introduced in the bicycling boom of the early 1890s by Parisian gunsmith Charles Galand, 'Velo-Dog' revolvers were the first of the European patterns to be developed for ammunition loaded with smokeless propellant. Cartridges of this type generated far higher pressure than the black-powder loadings, and so the guns were stronger than most of their predecessors. As the 5.5mm Velo-Dog cartridge had an unusually long straight-sided case, the revolvers are customarily identifiable by the excessive length of

their cylinders. A special 6mm 'Type Française' rimfire cartridge was sometimes offered as an alternative, guns of this type sharing the long cylinders.

DOUBLE-ACTION COLTS
The advent of efficient double-action cartridge revolvers eventually persuaded Colt's Patent Fire Arms Manufacturing Company to develop a gun of its own. The .38 or .41 Double Action Revolvers, now known as the 'Lightning' and 'Thunderer' respectively, were introduced at the beginning of 1877. Applied retrospectively in the early 1880s, the names were

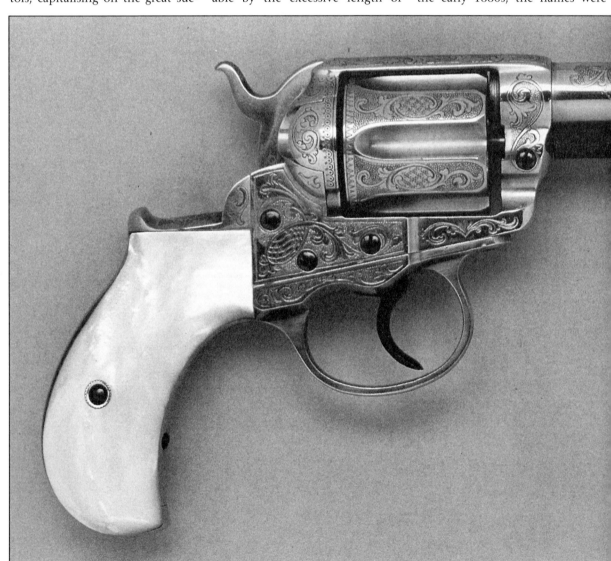

coined not by Colt's marketing department but by Benjamin Kittredge & Company of Cincinnati. The double-action mechanism, the work of William Mason, was too delicate to be durable, and the guns were dogged by breakages. The frame was similar to that of the Single Action Army Model ('Peacemaker'), but had a slender bird's-head butt instead of the square-heel type. Many surviving double-action Colts are nickel-plated, grips being chequered gutta-percha or carved from a single piece of rosewood. Barrel lengths could be as short as 1½in, though ejectors were omitted from

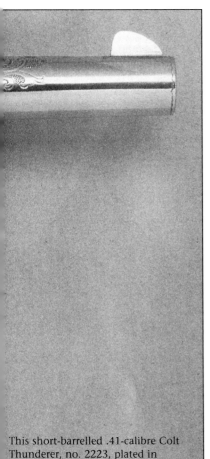

This short-barrelled .41-calibre Colt Thunderer, no. 2223, plated in nickel and gold, formed part of the award-winning display of H.D. Folsom & Co. at the 1877 St Louis Exposition. It was sold by auctioneers Butterfield & Butterfield of San Francisco in 1996.

barrels measuring less than 4½in. A .32 Long centre-fire chambering was offered for a few years, but was very unpopular commercially.

The Double Action Army & Frontier Model Colt was similar to the Lightning, improved in accordance with a new 1881-vintage Mason patent. The shape of the rear of the frame differed greatly. Blueing and walnut grips were standard, though nickel plating was optional and guns will be found with grips of rubber, ivory, or pearl. Short-barrel ejectorless "Sheriff's" or 'House' patterns could be ordered with spurless hammers, which were unlikely to snag on clothing.

EASIER LOADING

There were several obvious solutions to reducing the time required to reload a revolver of Peacemaker type by inserting cartridges painstakingly one-by-one through a gate. A pointer to the future had clearly been provided by the .22 Smith & Wesson Model No. 1, with the barrel and frame latched together to allow the cylinder to be removed when required. These revolvers had been extensively copied in Europe even before the American Civil War had ended, and it was in Europe that real enthusiasm for quick-loading systems first took hold. The initial steps were many and varied, characteristic of the approach taken by gunmakers in England, Belgium, France and Spain for many years. Whereas the North American market was dominated by demands for reliability, which meant a preference for simple and sturdy guns, the European fascination with technology often promoted solutions which were mechanically elegant but complicated to handle or difficult to make.

One of the most influential of the earliest designs was the Galand & Somerville revolver, patented in Britain in 1868 and adopted by the Imperial Russian Navy in the early 1870s. Guns made in Birmingham for the commercial market will

often be found with the marks of British retailers, such as Holland & Holland or James Dougall of London. A hinged lever forged integrally with the trigger guard could be pulled downwards, moving the cylinder forward and away from the standing breech. An extractor plate ensured that the chambered cartridges were withdrawn sufficiently far for spent cases to fall clear of the gun. Most Galand & Somerville revolvers were far too large to be genuinely pocketable, but Galand himself made five-chamber guns in chamberings as small as 7mm centre-fire.

Martin & Co. of Liége made revolvers, including some folding-trigger pocket guns, with a barrel/cylinder which could be lifted upwards once the latch under the front of the frame had been released. Guns marked HILL'S PATENT embody a similar lifting barrel system, but have an ejector which is activated automatically. They were apparently made in accordance with a patent granted in Britain in 1878 to William Hill of St Mary's Row, Birmingham (a gunsmith and sometime 'Vice-Consul for the Republic of Uruguay'), but had to be inverted to reload satisfactorily, inhibiting sales.

The most popular rapid-loading method was the dropping barrel, pioneered in the USA in the early 1870s by Smith & Wesson. The principal novelties concerned the design of the extractor/ejector mechanism and the precise design of the barrel latch.

A primitive dropping-barrel design, also made as a barrelless 'pepperbox', was patented by Jean-Baptiste Devisme of Paris in 1869, relying on a latch beneath the barrel to release the barrel/cylinder unit to tip down around a transverse pivot in front of the trigger guard. However, the British Webleys are undoubtedly the best known of the European break-open guns, refined stage-by-stage through a series of patents granted to Jean Warnant,

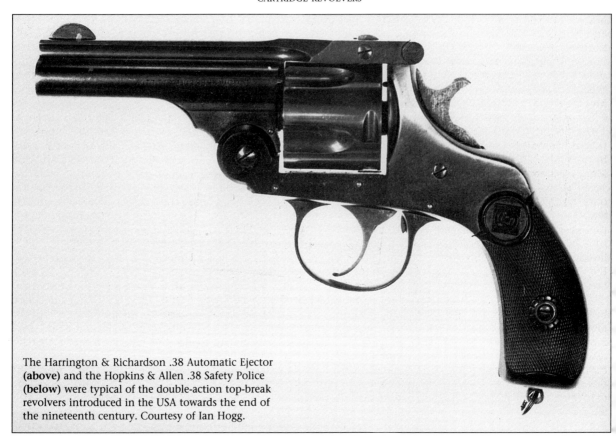

The Harrington & Richardson .38 Automatic Ejector
(above) and the Hopkins & Allen .38 Safety Police
(below) were typical of the double-action top-break
revolvers introduced in the USA towards the end of
the nineteenth century. Courtesy of Ian Hogg.

Michael Kaufmann, John Carter and William Whiting until perfection was reached.

Few early Webleys were truly pocketable until the emergence of the .320 six-shot Webley Pocket Model ('WP') in 1901 and an exposed-hammer New Model in 1906. Both patterns were discontinued about 1937, being replaced by the .320-calibre variant of the Mark III. They were about 6in long, with the shorter or 2in barrel option, and weighed about 16oz. One valuable guide to dating is provided by changes in the company name, which became the 'Webley & Scott Revolver & Arms Co. Ltd' in 1897 and 'Webley & Scott Ltd' in 1906.

Other guns of this general class included the Le Vaux, made in Belgium, with a top latch above the hammer. This could be pressed downwards to release the barrel-cylinder group to drop downwards. The Bernard, Francotte, Gillon and Warnant systems, all Belgian, had dropping barrels; the Deville, made in Liége, relied on a lever to move the barrel/cylinder unit away from the breech; and a lever under the frame of the Mercennier could be turned laterally, allowing the cylinder/barrel group to tip to the right before being pulled forward to expel spent cases. These systems are explained in detail in *The Revolver 1865–1888* and *The Revolver 1888–1914* by Anthony Taylerson, which are rightly regarded as classic works in their field.

Among the most influential of the first American double-action revolvers, Smith & Wessons excepted, were guns based on patents granted in 1874–8 to Benjamin Williams, Daniel Moore and William Hulbert. Made exclusively in the Hopkins & Allen factory in Norwich, Connecticut, they were sold only by Merwin, Hulbert & Company and Hulbert Brothers & Company, sporting-goods distributors based in New York.

The revolver barrel, integral with the upper part of the frame,

was attached to the standing breech by the cylinder axis-pin and a lock on the frame ahead of the trigger guard. When the catch was released, the barrel could be swung laterally. Moving the barrel-block and cylinder forward allowed a star-plate extractor, attached to the breech, to withdraw the cartridges far enough for spent cases (but not unfired rounds) to fall clear. A sliding gate on the right side of the frame beneath the hammer permitted reloading.

A .44 centre-fire single-action Merwin & Hulbert was tried by the US Army in 1877, but its open-top frame was judged to be too weak for service. The first strengthened top-strap derivative was a five-shot centre-fire .38 with a sheath trigger, announced in 1879-80. The .44 Pocket Army Model, with a 3½in barrel and a bird's-head butt, was made without the top-strap (to use existing components) until a revised pattern appeared in the summer of 1882.

Merwin & Hulbert announced their first double-action revolver early in 1883. By 1884 the product range included the short-barrelled .44-40 Double Action Pocket Army, weighing 36oz, and the five-chamber .38 S&W Triumph with barrels of 3½in or 5½in. Triumph-type revolvers may still be found with a distinctive folding hammer.

No double-action S&W was made in quantity until the Colt Lightning appeared early in 1878. This forced Daniel Wesson and James Bullard to compete, Bullard completing a break-open auto-ejecting .32 revolver design in February 1879 and a similar .38 in October. As the Colt was available in .38 and .41, Smith & Wesson initially concentrated on the .38 Double Action. A catalogue printed in 1880 offered the new five-shot '.38/100' revolver with barrels of 3½–5in. Blue or nickel finishes were available, moulded black gutta-percha grips being standard. The detachable side plate fitted to the original Double Action Smith & Wesson revolver ran completely

across the frame. After 4,000 guns had been made, the frame was strengthened by the substitution of a smaller plate, and 115,000 highly successful second-pattern S&W .38 Double Action revolvers were made in 1880–4.

The third pattern had an improved cylinder stop, eliminating the double row of cylinder-stop slots. About 204,000 guns had been made by 1895. The fourth variation – made until 1909 – had an improved sear, though the change was impossible to detect externally. Production of this sub-variant had exceeded 216,000 when the fifth and final version appeared. About 15,000 fifth-pattern .38 Smith & Wessons had been completed when work finally ceased in 1911. They were distinguishable by a squared barrel catch and front sights forged integrally with the barrel.

Designed by Joseph Wesson and introduced in 1909, the .38 Perfected Model was a top-break derivative of the contemporaneous .32 Hand Ejector. The guns had a conventional oval trigger guard instead of the reverse-curve pattern associated with the earlier .38 patterns. The Perfected Model also had a sliding thumb-latch on the frame behind the recoil shield, locking the cylinder shut with additional security. It was discontinued soon after the end of the First World War, when nearly 60,000 had been made with barrels ranging from 3½in to 6in.

The first few .32 Double Actions were assembled in May 1880, nearly 10,000 of the 14oz five-shot guns being made by the end of the year. Virtually all of them were nickel plated. The original barrel-lengths were 3in or 3½in, a 6in version being added in 1882. The original pattern of 1880, now very rarely encountered, had a full-width side plate which weakened the frame. The second or small-plate variation was much more popular, production amounting to about 22,000 by 1882. The third model had an improved cylinder stop, but only 21,230 were made in 1882–3. The fourth-type .38 (1883–1909) introduced an oval trigger guard instead of the original reverse-curve type. Several internal improvements were also made. Nearly 240,000 of these guns were made, plus about 44,600 fifth-pattern guns (1909–19) with their front sights forged integrally with the barrel.

The commercial importance of these break-open Smith & Wessons is implicit in the production total, which was approaching a million when work ceased in 1920.

LESSER DOUBLE-ACTION REVOLVERS

Although Colt and Smith & Wesson were acknowledged as the market leaders in the 1880s, smaller manufacturers were often much more daring. Among them was Iver Johnson & Company, created in 1883 to become 'Iver Johnson Arms & Cycle Works' within a year. The 'Model 1879' Iver Johnson revolver of 1883, initially chambered only for .38 Smith & Wesson cartridges, was the first American-made double-action revolver to feature a cylinder which could be swung laterally to reload. The mechanism was protected by patents issued in 1879–83 to Andrew Hyde of Hatfield, Massachusetts, but the Model 1879 was expensive for an Iver Johnson product and failed to find a substantial market. It disappeared after only a few years.

US Makers of Double-action Pocket Revolvers

NOTE: guns may be encountered under misleading names – e.g., Model 1892 Smith revolvers were handled by the sporting-goods suppliers Maltby, Henley & Company of New York City and marked as products of the spurious 'Columbia Armory', 'Spencer Revolver Company' or 'Parker Revolver Company'.

Foehl & Weeks Manufacturing Company, Philadelphia, Pennsylvania
Columbian, Perfect.

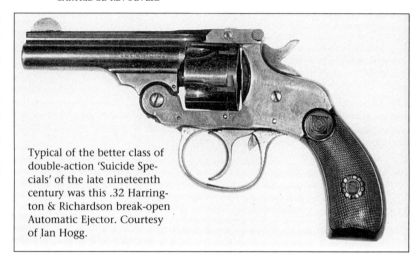

Typical of the better class of double-action 'Suicide Specials' of the late nineteenth century was this .32 Harrington & Richardson break-open Automatic Ejector. Courtesy of Ian Hogg.

Harrington & Richardson's .22 Young American revolver typified the inexpensive double-action solid-frame designs introduced before 1914. Courtesy of Ian Hogg.

Andrew Fyrberg & Company, Hopkinton, Massachusetts
Harrington & Richardson Arms Company, Worcester, Massachusetts
Automatic Ejecting Model, Bicycle, Police Automatic, Police Bicycle Model, Police Premier, Premier,
Hopkins & Allen Arms Company, Norwich, Connecticut
Acme, Automatic Model, Forehand Model, XL DA series.
Iver Johnson's Arms & Cycle Works, Fitchburg, Massachusetts
American Bull Dog, Boston Bull Dog, Swift, U.S. Double Action.
J. M. Marlin Fire Arms Company, New Haven, Connecticut
Meriden Firearms Company, Meriden,

Connecticut
Otis Smith, Rock Fall, Connecticut

HAMMERLESS GUNS

The ease with which the spur of a conventional external hammer could catch in clothing presented the designers of pocket revolvers with a serious problem. Some simply provided a folding spur, a cheap but often unacceptable solution, while others sought something much more radical. The enclosed-hammer or 'hammerless' revolvers were one of the most important results.

The first hammerless Smith & Wessons were based on existing double-action break-open guns, the

The .32 Safety Hammerless pocket revolver, also known as the 'New Departure' or 'Lemon Squeezer', was announced in the spring of 1888. It was little more than a smaller version of the .38 Safety Hammerless, except that the first-pattern .32 resembled the third-model .38 (though it lacked the internal safety). A small button-type barrel latch protruded from the top strap. More than 90,000 guns were made in 1888-1902. The standard barrels measured 3in or 3½in, but a 2in option was introduced in 1902 and a 6in version appeared in 1904. The second .32 had a 'T'-type barrel latch, with knurled-head buttons; the third model offered minor internal changes. About 150,000 of these were made in 1902–9 and 1909–37 respectively.

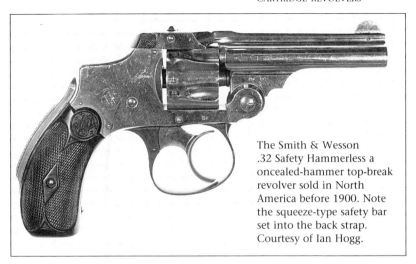

The Smith & Wesson .32 Safety Hammerless a oncealed-hammer top-break revolver sold in North America before 1900. Note the squeeze-type safety bar set into the back strap. Courtesy of Ian Hogg.

An alternative approach was taken in the Police Automatic revolver introduced in 1897 by the Harrington & Richardson Arms Company of Worcester, Massachusetts. This gun had a spurless 'safety hammer' patented in October 1887 by Homer Caldwell, which allowed thumb-cocking only after the trigger had been pressed to raise the hammer to half cock. Harrington & Richardson also made enclosed-hammer pocket revolvers in two sizes. The small-frame five-shot .32 had barrels of 3–in and weighed only 13oz; the larger version was offered as a six-shot .32 or a five-shot .38.

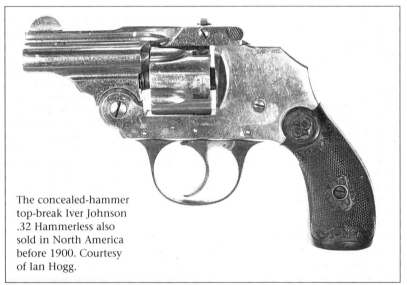

The concealed-hammer top-break Iver Johnson .32 Hammerless also sold in North America before 1900. Courtesy of Ian Hogg.

frame being raised behind the cylinder to envelop the hammer. The design perfected by Joseph Wesson in 1886 had an inertia-type firing pin and a spring-loaded safety plate set into the back strap of the butt. Although large-calibre prototypes were made, the first to be made in quantity was the .38 Safety Hammerless Revolver. Distinguished by a Z-bar latch set in the top strap above the cylinder, about 5,250 emanated from the Springfield factory in 1886–7. Improvements were then made in the barrel latch, and work continued until 1890; about 32,000 of these second-pattern guns were made. However, constant problems with the barrel latch led to the substitution of a knurled thumb-piece pinned into the top strap and the addition of an auxiliary safety system to prevent the gun firing as it was being opened. More than 70,000 of these third-pattern guns had been made by 1898.

The fourth model had a knurled-head barrel latch, about 104,000 being made in 1898–1907. The fifth and last variant was identical with its predecessor, except that the front sight was integral with the barrel and some minor adjustments were made internally. The last of 41,500 fifth-pattern revolvers did not leave Springfield until 1940.

A TRIAL OF STRENGTH

As cartridges grew more powerful, the break-open frame guns marketed by Smith & Wesson and others were unable to cope with the increased pressures. The double-action Colts had been praised for their solid frames, but the lockwork was too delicate to attract approval either from the US Army or commercial purchasers.

A revolver patented in 1879–83 by Andrew Hyde of Hatfield, Massachusetts, was the first solid-frame swinging-cylinder pattern to be offered commercially in the USA. A few guns chambering the .38 Smith & Wesson centre-fire cartridge were made by the Iver Johnson Arms & Cycle Works in the mid-1880s, but were too expensive to appeal to a clientele which expected simple and inexpensive products.

The first advance to be made by Colt came in the form of a patent granted in December 1881 to William Mason, protecting a solid-frame revolver with a cylinder which swung laterally. Trials suggested that several improvements would be beneficial, a series of patents to William Mason, Jean Warnant, Carl Ehbets and Horace Lord being granted in 1884–8. Five thousand .38-calibre Navy Model 1889 revolvers were eventually ordered from Colt, but the initial enthusiasm was not matched by performance in service. The cylinder and the cylinder yoke both turned to the left, and excessive wear eventually meant that the chambers and the barrel locked out of alignment.

Changes were made in the Model 1892 Army revolver, but it was soon discovered that the gun could be fired before the cylinder was properly locked into the frame. A safety interlock was hastily developed by Frederick Felton, creating the Model 1894, and the rotation of the cylinder was finally reversed in 1901.

The military-style Colts were much too large to be pocketable, but the success of the swinging-cylinder loading system encouraged production of smaller guns. The first of these was the six-shot New Pocket Model of 1893, chambered for .32 Colt, .32 Smith & Wesson or .32 New Police cartridges. The revolvers shared many features with the contemporaneous .38 Double Action Army Revolver (M1892), but the cylinder rotated to the right. The guns had small frames, befitting their power; the shortest of the barrels was just 2½in long, but most purchasers chose the 4in or 6in options which reduced pocketability. Minor improvements in the lockwork were made during a production life spanning twelve years, together with the introduction of an improved chequered-head cylinder latch. Walnut grips were replaced by chequered gutta-percha patterns, with the company name moulded into the neck. The enthusiasm for the small Colts was limited by the price, which was high compared with many rival designs. This restricted production to about 31,000 by 1905.

The .32 New Police Model Colt is said to have been developed in 1896 to satisfy Theodore Roosevelt, who was then Commissioner of the New York Police Department. It was simply the New Pocket model with a longer grip; almost 50,000 were made in 1896–1907 with plain walnut or chequered gutta-percha 'COLT' grips. The designation appeared on the left side of the frame beneath the hammer, curved around a rampant colt motif. This eventually became the colt backed by the letter 'C', and then simply the colt itself.

The .32 Police Positive Model replaced the New Police Model after 1905, almost 200,000 having been made by the end of production in 1943. The small-calibre Colts soon proved to be poor man-stoppers, however, and ultra-short barrels degraded performance even further. One answer was found simply by enlarging the calibre. The Police Positive Special Model of 1907 chambered .38 Special cartridges (.32-20 WCF was optional) and had a longer cylinder than the .32 Police Positive. Barrels initially measured 4-6in, though a 2in 'Snub Nose' option was added in 1926.

Declining sales of traditional break-open guns, which were perceived as obsolescent, forced Smith & Wesson to follow the path flagged by Colt. The .32 Smith & Wesson Hand Ejector Model and the accompanying .32 S&W Long cartridge appeared in 1896. A split-spring unit in the top strap locked the six-chamber cylinder, which could be swung out to the left of the solid frame once the head of the ejector rod had been pulled forward to release the yoke. The shortest barrel option was 3½in, just enough to make the revolver pocketable. However, most purchasers preferred longer barrels.

The Hand Ejector was not a great success, which reflected the popular association of Smith & Wesson with break-open guns. Only about 19,000 had been made when an improved 'Model 1903' was introduced. This had a distinctive thumb latch on the left side of the frame, behind the recoil shield, locking the cylinder at both ends of the ejector rod. An improved cylinder-stop system was mounted in the bottom of the frame, above the trigger, and a round barrel was fitted. Five major changes had been made to the new Hand Ejector by 1910, production ceasing in 1917 after about 263,000 had been made. The Third Model Hand Ejector, similar externally to the fifth-change M1903, had an additional hammer-block safety in the trigger system.

THE QUEST FOR GREATER SAFETY

The widespread introduction of double-action trigger systems was a major contribution to personal defence, as it permitted the development of pocket revolvers which could be pulled from a pocket and fired 'on the draw'. However, the increasing popularity of these guns was accompanied by a rise in accidents. Most were insignificant, but a handful proved to be fatal. The principal problems were the snagging of the hammer in the pocket, trigger systems which were either badly made or badly adjusted, and the chance of firing a gun with a blow on the hammer after a cartridge had been chambered.

The development of hammerless revolvers cured the snagging problems but prevented the firer thumb-cocking the hammer. As it was well known that firing a gun in this 'single-action' manner improved accuracy, the hammerless revolvers did not become especially popular in North America. An interesting attempt to circumvent this problem was made by George Fox and Henry Wheeler, who, in March 1890, obtained a patent protecting an enclosed hammer mechanism which could be rotated to full-cock by one pull of the trigger and then released by a second. A selector on the frame-side allowed the firer to revert to conventional double action when necessary. Guns of this pattern were made in small quantities by the American Arms Company of Boston, Massachusetts (before 1893), and Milwaukee, Wisconsin (working 1893– 1901).

Few of the perfected break-open designs could be fired until the breech was securely locked, but the same could not always be said of the solid-frame guns. Even the first swinging-cylinder Colts could be fired before the cylinder was locked shut, forcing the hasty introduction (in 1894) of the Felton interlock system. Gradually, therefore, mechanical safety grew in importance.

An early leader in this particular field was Iver Johnson's Arms & Cycle Works of Fitchburg, Massachusetts. A series of conventional double-action revolvers culminating in the Swift of 1891 had failed to make a lasting impact in the crowded market-place, and something different was sought. This was found by placing a spacer between the hammer and the firing pin to transfer the blow only when the trigger was deliberately pulled. The first .38-calibre Safety Automatic Revolvers seem to have been introduced about 1892, selling steadily for some years without capturing public attention.

In the spring of 1904, however, Frederick Iver Johnson sought the advice of the George Batten Company. William Johns, an agency vice-president, called at Johnson's New York office to discuss publicity. After showing brochures, flyers and advertisements to his visitor, Johnson asked Johns to comment on the content. Johns had noticed the recurrent phrase 'Accidental Discharge Impossible', and remarked that it was a shame that the Iver Johnson company made capital out of such a misleading claim.

Above: The famous 'Hammer-the-Hammer' feature distinguished many of the Iver Johnson revolvers, and was widely used in the company's advertising.

Frederick Johnson was aghast. He sent for an Automatic Safety revolver, loaded it, then threw it with great force against the office safe, ten feet away. He banged it hard on the table, kicked it around the office, then struck the hammer with the gun pointing at his own leg. Johns subsequently recollected that he had been speechless with terror, but had eventually persuaded Johnson to stop mistreating the gun. However, the advertising executive was well aware than few rival designs would have survived such a pounding. He suggested that much more attention could be

drawn to the safety system, and the resulting 'Hammer the Hammer' slogan was used for more than 70 years.

Coil springs were used for the first time in 1908, and an adjustable mainspring tension bar, with a ball-and-socket joint, was added to connect the mainspring plunger with the hammer. The Iver Johnson revolvers were offered in .32 and .38, with barrels of 4in or 6in.

There is no doubt that this astute copywriting raised Iver Johnson's status dramatically. A company which had been in the doldrums could claim by 1909 that output of its revolvers exceeded the combined production of all the other US manufacturers. This apparently went unchallenged, as the production of three million Safety Automatic revolvers prior to 1911 could not be denied. Catalogues were being distributed throughout the world in eight languages.

The publicity gained by the Hammer-the-Hammer system was so great that the absence of comparable safety features from even well-respected designs soon elicited adverse comment. Thus the 1893-type Colt New Pocket revolver was superseded by the .32 Pocket Positive Model of 1905, embodying a new Positive Safety Lock to interpose a bar between the hammer and the cartridge-head until the trigger was pressed. The last of about 130,000 Pocket Positive revolvers was assembled in 1943.

The Police Positive Model Colt of 1905 also embodied the Positive Lock safety system. The guns were handy, weighing only 16-21oz; barrels ranged from 2½in to 6in. Grips were chequered gutta-percha, originally with 'COLT' moulded into the neck but subsequently replaced by a decorative pattern with a stylised 'C' surrounding the retaining screws. The butt was lengthened soon after introduc-

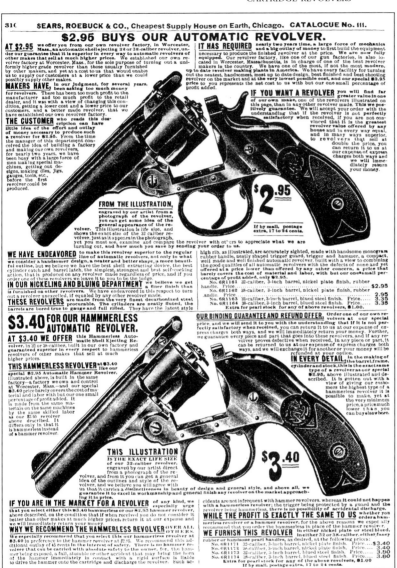

Left: A selection of American-made auto-ejecting revolvers advertised in the catalogue published by Sears, Roebuck & Co. at the turn of the century.

tion, improving grip, and the frame was enlarged in 1925.

Another approach was taken by the Hopkins & Allen Arms Company, which had been created in 1898 out of a long-established gun-making business. The new company survived a disastrous fire to acquire Forehand & Wadsworth in 1902. The Hopkins & Allen Automatic Model revolver was replaced in 1907 by the Safety Police Model. Eventually sold in .22, .32 and .38, this retained the frame and ejector of the Automatic Model but introduced the 'Triple Action Safety Lock' based on a patent granted in August 1906 to John Murphy of Norwich, Connecticut. The hammer was mounted on an eccentric pin which, when the hammer was down, raised the tip of the hammer to rest on a shoulder in the frame. The eccentric rotated as the trigger was pressed, changing the hammer-fall arc until the firing pin could be struck. The Triple Action Safety was very efficient, but only a few guns had been made before the outbreak of the First World War brought Hopkins & Allen some lucrative military orders.

The Smith & Wesson .32 Regulation Police and .38/32 Regulation Police revolvers of 1917, built on the light 'I' frame, both derived from the original Hand Ejector design. They were distinguished by large square-heel butts.

THE REVOLVER AFTER 1918
The aftermath of the First World War, supposedly a period of uni-

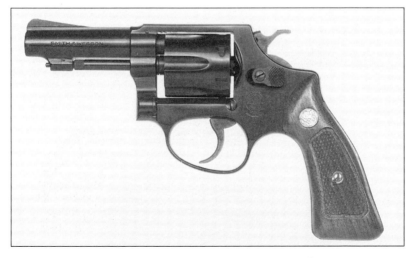

Left: This Smith & Wesson Model 31 is typical of the small-calibre revolvers favoured by police forces during the Depression and the Prohibition era. However, they were poor man-stoppers and were eventually replaced by more effective weapons. Courtesy of Smith & Wesson.

versal peace, was not an era in which attention was paid to handguns. However, the needs of police forces (not to mention the underworld) ensured that established designs continued to be made on a reduced scale.

Very few significant changes were made, 'new models' being little more than minor adaptations of existing designs. Typical of these were the Colt Detective Special and Banker's Special, introduced in 1926 and 1928 respectively, which were derivatives of the Police Positive Special with 2in barrels and shortened ejector rods. The difference lay in the butts, the Detective Special having a short round-heel pattern instead of the full-length squared design.

The collapse of Wall Street in 1929 and the ensuing Depression was not conducive to investment. Many smaller American manufacturers found the inter-war period difficult to negotiate; though most of the better-known participants managed to survive, only Colt and Smith & Wesson retained a real foothold in the military and police market.

Among the most important events in this period was the introduction in 1935 of the .357 Smith & Wesson Magnum cartridge and an accompanying heavy-frame Hand Ejector revolver. Intended for long-range hunting and sporting use, the Magnum was initially regarded as much too powerful for

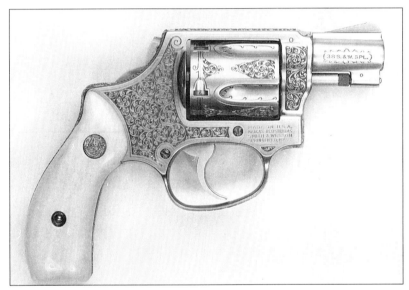

Top and above: Two short-barrelled .38 Smith & Wesson revolvers, distinguished by scroll engraving. Note the 'bobbed' or spurless hammer on the lower illustration, which has been a popular way of preventing guns snagging in pockets or holsters during the draw.

Right: Many of the cheap solid-frame revolvers made in recent years are little more than modernised versions of the pre-1914 guns. This .22 rimfire Harrington & Richardson Model 930 is typical of many guns made since the end of the Second World War.

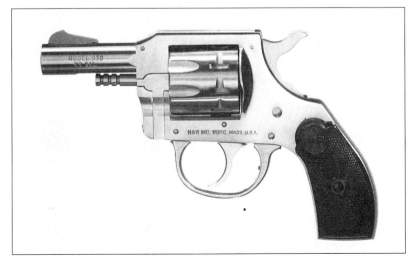

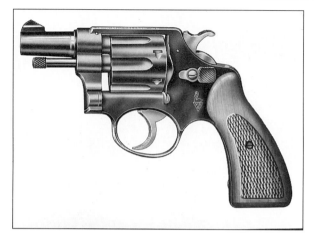

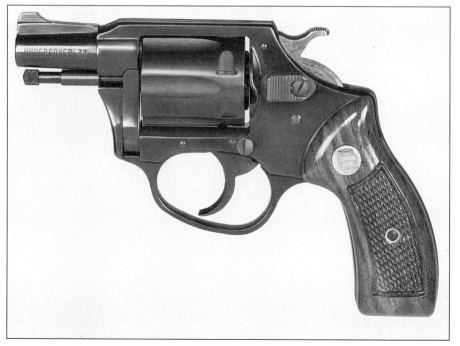

Typical Smith & Wesson-type pocket revolvers. **Top left:** Italian-made .38 Bernardelli. **Top right:** A Spanish Llama Model 32 ('XXXII'). **Centre left:** A Brazilian Forjas Taurus Model 85. **Centre right:** A German .38 Special Erma-Revolver ER440. **Left:** An American .32 S&W Long 'Undercover', made by Charter Arms.

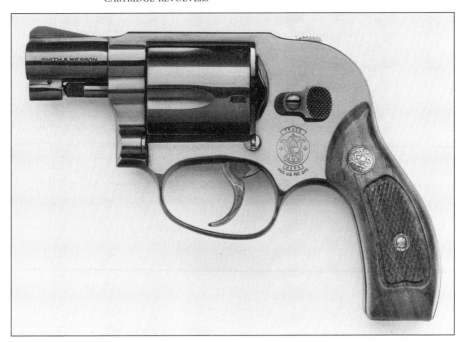

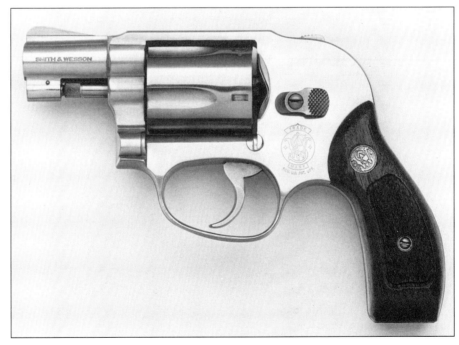

Smith & Wesson Models 49 **(right)** and 649 **(lower right)** have their hammers concealed inside the raised frame. Both are shown with 2in barrels. Courtesy of Smith & Wesson, Spring-field, Massachusetts.

personal-defence use. The recoil was considerable, and muzzle blast was particularly severe in a short barrel. After the Second World War, how-ever, perceptions changed; instead of demanding low-power revolvers which could be shot accurately, police forces (and, increasingly, the commercial market) clamoured for better stopping power. Even the .38 Special cartridge, considered by many observers to be the optimum for ultra-short-barrelled guns, was overtaken by the .357 Magnum. Colt chambered the latter in a mod-ernised Detective Special known as the Cobra, introduced in 1950, and then in a series of similar guns whose descendants survive in the 1990s. The Lawman Mark III of 1969 and the Lawman Mark V of 1982 have both been restricted to the Magnum cartridge, even though the barrel length is customarily only 3in.

Smith & Wesson initially con-centrated on .38-calibre revolvers,

Left: The Llama Piccolo revolver, made in Spain, has a cylinder-locking system based on that of the Colt instead of the generally more popular Smith & Wesson. It is shown with a speed-loader (top) and the special key (bottom left) which can be used to lock the firing mechanism. The locking spindle may be seen in the frame directly above the trigger.

Top right: The advent of powerful Magnum ammunition inspired a range of compact but extremely powerful double-action revolvers. This Smith & Wesson Model 624, with a 3in barrel, is not suited to the novice.

Bottom right: Some gunmakers have preferred traditional big-bore chamberings instead of high-pressure Magnums. Typical of this approach is this .44 special five-shot Charter Arms 'Law Enforcement Bulldog' with a 3in barrel, a bobbed Pocket Hammer and wrap-around Neoprene grips.

including the Model 36 Chief's Special of 1950 and the Model 12 Military & Police Airweight of 1952. The Chief's Special, also offered with a lightweight alloy frame (Model 37) or in stainless steel (Model 60), has been particularly popular for covert use. The Model 49 Bodyguard, introduced in 1955, is a similar design with an enclosed hammer.

An attempt was made to market the Model 547 personal-defence revolver in 9mm Parabellum, with a sharply curved grip to handle the increased recoil, but the project was not especially successful and was rapidly abandoned. Much more popular has been the Model 28 Highway Patrolman, a .357 Magnum design with a 4in barrel.

The American designs have been copied in vast numbers, particularly in Spain, where the first Smith & Wesson clones were being pro-duced even before the patents had expired. Most of the revolvers being made today by Astra and Llama-Gabilondo in Spain, Taurus in Brazil or Rossi in Argentina are still little more than Smith & Wessons internally.

The advent in 1968 of the Gun Control Act, which made transfer-bar safety systems obligatory on guns sold in the USA, removed many lesser designs from the North American market. How-

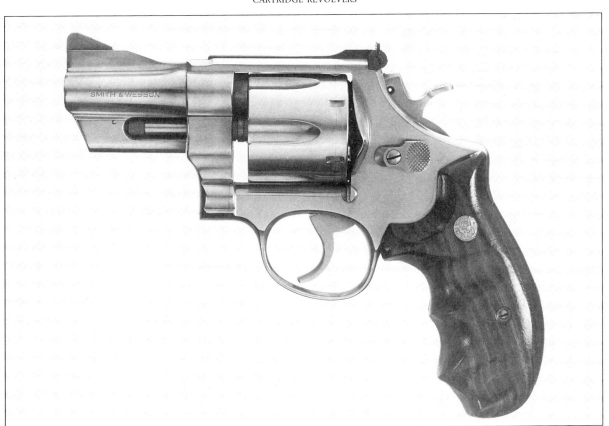

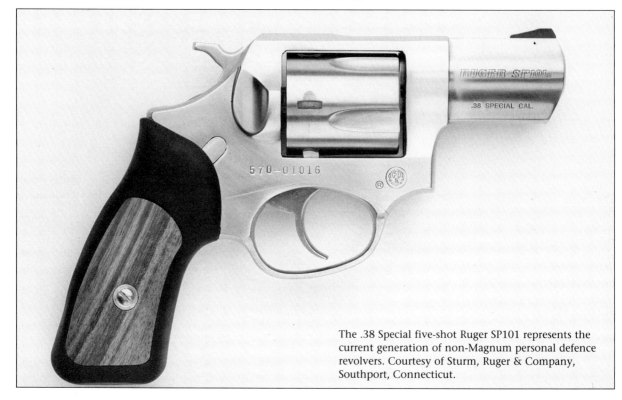

The .38 Special five-shot Ruger SP101 represents the current generation of non-Magnum personal defence revolvers. Courtesy of Sturm, Ruger & Company, Southport, Connecticut.

ever, manufacturers such as Sturm, Ruger and Charter Arms, to name but two, have produced many efficient personal-defence weapons.

Though ground has been steadily lost to the large-magazine automatic pistol in the USA, the revolver's last real stronghold, many experienced commentators still consider mechanical operation superior to any system which relies on the proper ignition of individual cartridges to function satisfactorily. It seems most unlikely that the cartridge revolver has had its final hour.

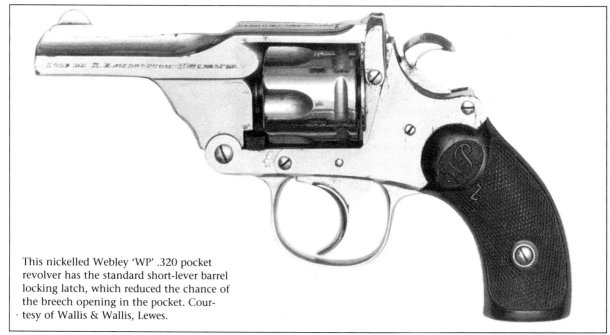

This nickelled Webley 'WP' .320 pocket revolver has the standard short-lever barrel locking latch, which reduced the chance of the breech opening in the pocket. Courtesy of Wallis & Wallis, Lewes.

REPEATING PISTOLS

The idea of a repeating firearm dates back to the wheel-lock era, when single-barrel/multi-chamber rifles had been made in an effort to reduce the weight of multi-barrel alternatives while avoiding dangerous superimposed charges.

SINGLE FIXED-BARREL DESIGNS

The earliest single-barrel repeaters were too sophisticated for their period, as were later disc-breech flintlocks made on the Lorenzoni system. These included a few pistols. Interest in multi-shot weapons persisted, but was often satisfied simply by fitting several full-length barrels. Typical of these were the Duck's Foot pistol of the late eighteenth century, with its barrels splayed to broaden the field of fire, and the nineteenth-century pepperboxes.

The revolver was the first single-barrel repeater to be made in quantity. However, though they could be fired very quickly, the cap-lock types were slow to load. The earliest rimfire cartridges were too weak, and pinfire rivals were easy to ignite accidentally.

A radical solution in the form of entirely self-contained ammunition, dispensing with a cartridge case, was patented by Walter Hunt of New York in August 1849. Hunt's repeating rifle was intended to fire 'Rocket Balls', cylindro-conoidal lead projectiles filled with priming composition. The prototype rifle, much too complicated to succeed, was entrusted to gunsmith Lewis Jennings for improvement, and an appropriate patent was obtained on Christmas Day

1849. A few hundred rifles were subsequently made by Robbins & Lawrence, but the manufacturers withdrew when they failed to find a market. Railroad magnate Courtlandt Palmer, who had been financing the work, subsequently licensed the patents to a new partnership of Horace Smith and Daniel Wesson. In June 1854, therefore, Smith & Wesson opened a small workshop in Norwich, (Connecticut) to make handgun adaptations of the Jennings rifle. An improved design was soon patented, and series production began.

The Volcanic and other American designs

The lever-action pistols were loaded through a port cut near the

A typical 8mm Protector repeating pistol. Courtesy of Ian Hogg.

muzzle in the underside of the magazine tube. The projectiles were .31, .36 and .44 Rocket Balls. Guns were made in several sizes, with magazine capacities of 8–10 projectiles. Unfortunately for Smith & Wesson, the rocket balls were too small to be effective. Accuracy was very poor and, as mercuric fulminate was exceptionally corrosive, the bores deteriorated rapidly unless cleaned regularly.

Keen to exploit a revolver patented by Rollin White, Smith & Wesson sold the rocket-ball patents to a syndicate of clockmakers, bakers, grocers, carriagemakers and entrepreneurs in the summer of 1855. In August the tools, fixtures, gauges and existing components were removed to New Haven, Connecticut, to form the Volcanic Repeating Fire Arms Company. True Volcanics, made before the sale of the company to Winchester, were invariably .40 calibre. These were pistols with ring-tipped operating levers, and carbines whose appearance foreshadowed the Henry rifle.

By midsummer 1857 the business was struggling once again. Sales had never been brisk, and the unstable fulminate powder, which sometimes blew the magazine tube off the breech, was proving a particular handicap. Charges of black powder cured the fault, but only with a marked loss of power.

The promise that lay in lever action and a tube magazine was hidden by the drawbacks of the Volcanic system. As Hunt, Palmer, and Smith & Wesson had all failed before it, so the Volcanic company also collapsed. Its assets were sold to Winchester, the New Haven Arms Company forming on 1 May 1857 to purchase the relevant patents. Guns continued to be known as 'Volcanic Repeating Fire Arms'. A broadsheet published in 1859 advertised, in addition to carbines and long-barrel .40 'Navy' pistols, a .31 pocket pistol with a 4in barrel and a six-ball magazine.

When the American Civil War broke out in 1861, the New Haven Arms Company was still facing catastrophe. Salvation was found in a lever-operated .44 rifle developed by Benjamin Henry, and work on the repeating pistols ceased in the early 1860s.

The failure of the Volcanic pistol did not entirely hide the potential of the repeating pistol. Accepting that the Rocket Ball would never challenge the metal-case cartridge, the Remington Arms Company tried a different, simpler approach with its Magazine Repeating Pistol. During 1872–88, 15,000 of these guns were made on the basis of a patent granted to Joseph Rider in August 1871. The sheath-trigger design had a tube magazine beneath the barrel for four .32 Extra Short rimfire cartridges. A fifth round could be loaded directly into the chamber. Rider's design relied on a variant of the proven rolling-block action and an elevator to convey cartridges to the breech. Most guns had 3in barrels and weighed 10oz. Some had colour case-hardened frames, while others were nickelled. The standard varnished walnut grips could be replaced to order by ivory or mother-of-pearl.

European patterns

Most of the repeating pistols developed in central Europe were much too large to be pocketable. Unfortunately, too little is known about the history of the 'Bohemian School', named after the area of Austria-Hungary where many of the inventors worked, to allow an adequate classification to be attempted.

European repeaters were normally locked by rotary bolts, operated by a ring-lever surrounding the trigger, but the relationships between them have yet to be resolved. For example, it has been suggested that the Bittner pistol, made in Weipert, may have been nothing other than a Passler & Seidl with a Reiger magazine.

A forward movement of the finger lever generally unlocked the bolt and moved it backward. Pulling the lever back returned the bolt, stripping a round from the magazine into the breech, then re-locked the mechanism for the next shot. The final backward movement of the finger lever sometimes tripped the firing pin automatically.

Though the repeaters were impossibly complicated, they were often very well made and could fire quite rapidly if they were kept clean. Their worst feature was undoubtedly a lack of adequate primary extraction.

One or two minuscule Bittner pistols have been reported, small enough almost to be considered pocketable; Francotte made a compact pistol with a ring trigger and a detachable box magazine in the butt, and the Belgian Counet pattern is also reasonably compact.

The semi-automatic pistol soon eclipsed the large mechanically-operated repeating pistols, yet some of the smaller versions fared surprisingly well. An oddity among single-barrel designs was the turret-type palm pistol patented by Frenchman Jacques-Edmond Turbiaux in 1882–3. Large numbers of these guns, known as 'Le Protecteur', were made in France for an underpowered but no less distinctive short-case 8mm centre-fire cartridge. Others enjoyed a short vogue in North America under the brand name 'Protector', often embodying improvements patented by Peter Finnegan of Austin, Illinois, in August 1893.

Made by the Ames Sword Company of Chicopee Falls, Massachusetts, the seven-shot .32 Short rimfire Protector was marketed initially by the Minneapolis Fire-Arms Company and then by the Chicago Fire Arms Company. A short barrel protruded between the firer's fingers from the frame or receiver, which contained a flat disc-like magazine. The gun was fired by pressing a spring-loaded plate at the back of the frame

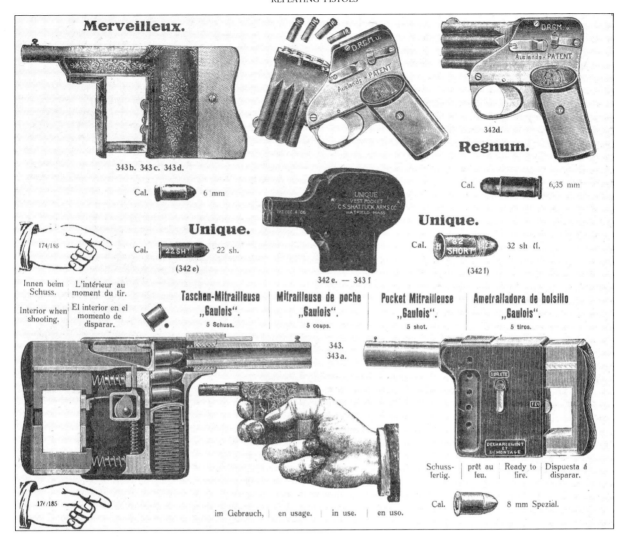

Merveilleux.

343b. 343c. 343d.

Cal. ● 6 mm

174/185

Innen beim Schuss. | L'intérieur au moment du tir.

Interior when shooting. | El interior en el momento de disparar.

Unique.

Cal. 22 SHT 22 sh.

(342 e)

342e. — 343 f

Taschen-Mitrailleuse „Gaulois". | **Mitrailleuse de poche „Gaulois".** | **Pocket Mitrailleuse „Gaulois".** | **Ametralladora de bolsillo „Gaulois".**
5 Schuss. | 5 coups. | 5 shot. | 5 tiros.

343. 343 a.

176/185

im Gebrauch, | en usage. | in use. | en uso.

Regnum.

342d.

Cal. ● 6,35 mm

Unique.

Cal. 32 SHORT 32 sh tf.

(342 f)

Schuss-fertig. | prêt au feu. | Ready to fire. | Dispuesta á disparar.

Cal. ● 8 mm Spezial.

Above: A selection of repeating pistols, from the A. L. Frank ('ALFA') catalogue of 1911. Note the Gaulois and the decorative Merveilleux, probably made by Rouchouse of Saint-Étienne.

against the base of the firer's palm. Protectors usually had several finger spurs on the front surface of the frame, alongside the barrel, to improve the handgrip.

Most Minneapolis-made guns had manual safety levers, whereas the Chicago examples relied on squeezing the trigger lever to disengage an automatic safety on the finger spur. The guns were loaded by removing the side plate. Some Chicago-made Protectors have a distinctive double-ring finger guard designed about 1900 by John Norris of Springfield, Ohio; this prevented painful accidents by keeping the fingers away from the muzzle of the ultra-short barrel. Catalogues issued by Hartley & Graham in 1892 suggest that the Minneapolis Protector was made in three patterns: nickel-plated or blued, with rubber or pearl 'sides'.

Le Protecteur and its US-made cousin achieved limited distribution commercially, but were unable to compete with the popular pocket revolvers. The repeaters with box magazines were much more successful, particularly the 'Mitrailleuse à Poche' patented in France in August 1892 by Étienne Mimard and Pierre Blachon. Manufacture Française d'Armes et Cycles de Saint-Étienne began production of the Mitrailleuse in 1893 and continued work for almost twenty years.

The gun consisted of a box-like frame with a barrel at the front and a sliding grip at the back. The magazine held five 8mm Le Protecteur-type cartridges. The firer squeezed with the heel of his thumb, sliding the grip inward to strip a round from the magazine into the chamber, cock the striker, lock the breech, and then release the striker to fire the gun. When the spring-loaded grip was released, the spent case was automatically withdrawn from the chamber and thrown clear.

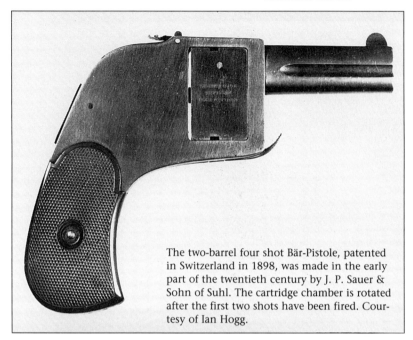

The two-barrel four shot Bär-Pistole, patented in Switzerland in 1898, was made in the early part of the twentieth century by J. P. Sauer & Sohn of Suhl. The cartridge chamber is rotated after the first two shots have been fired. Courtesy of Ian Hogg.

The Mitrailleuse worked surprisingly well and, as a result, enjoyed considerable popularity. The cartridge had to be very weak to allow the locking system to work properly, but the bullet was seated in the chamber at the moment of discharge to avoid the gas leaks customary in revolvers. A defective cartridge could be ejected mechanically without interrupting the operating sequence.

Originally marked MITRAILL-EUSE on top of the barrel rib, the repeaters were renamed 'Gaulois' in 1896 and marked appropriately. Production may have been surprisingly large, though claims in excess of one million should be treated with caution in view of the scarcity of survivors. Manufrance may simply have numbered all of its products in a single sequence. Catalogues suggest that the 1900-vintage Gaulois was produced in four models, ranging from the Model 1, polished and browned, with an ebonite grip, to the de luxe Model 4, which was chiselled, damascened and had a grip of ivory. Markings generally included the manufacturer's name, GAULOIS and an 'MF' monogram trademark. The pistols were very compact,

only about 14mm thick, and were often hidden in what, at first glance, appeared to be a leather cigar case.

The 8mm Rouchouse was another French design. The name is often said to have been an erroneous version of 'Rough-house', but the guns were made by J. Rouchouse & Cie of Saint-Étienne, successors to Manufacture d'Armes Escoffier in the 1880s. Known as

the 'Merveilleux', the pistol employed a variation of the Gaulois principle, with the grip unit sliding backwards into the frame. It would have been easier to shoot than its rival, owing to backward movement, towards the palm, and the addition of a shaped pad on the back of the frame. However, it was never popular and very little is known about its history except that it was still being advertised in 1914. The Merveilleux may simply have appeared too late to exert influence commercially.

Patented by Catello Tribuzio of Turin in the early 1890s, the Lampo had a distinctive ring trigger protruding from the lower front edge of its sculptured frame. Sliding the trigger backwards with the second finger of the firing hand operated the action in much the same way as the Gaulois, though the motion was somewhat easier. The 8mm Le Protecteur cartridge was retained.

The basic squeezer principle has been resurrected in recent years in Hungary, and is currently being

Below and right: Does the Hungarian MiniMax-9 herald a return to the era of the squeezer-type mechanical repeater? Courtesy of Ian Hogg.

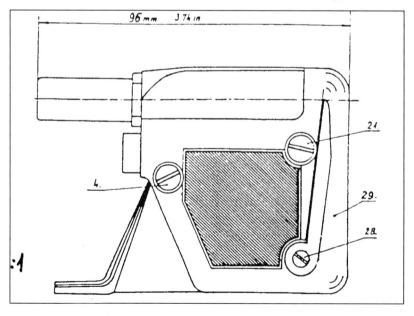

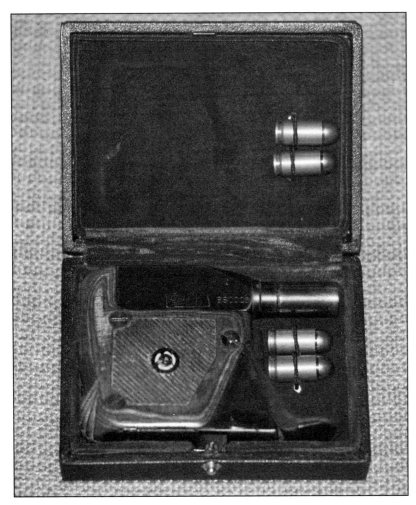

marketed as the 'MiniMax-9' in 9mm Short, 9mm Makarov and 9mm Parabellum. The grip slides backwards towards the palm, providing a surprisingly compact four-shot weapon measuring 96mm x 68mm x 24mm and weighing merely 360gm (9mm Short) or 420gm (9mm Parabellum). Even the larger five-shot 9mm Parabellum version is only 130mm long. Among the advantages claimed for the MiniMax-9 are small size in relation to its barrel length or power, one-hand operation, permanent readiness to fire, and an absence of springs in its construction.

Made by J. P. Sauer & Sohn of Suhl in the first few years of the twentieth century, the Bär-Pistole was patented by Burkhard Behr of Zürich in March 1898. Its claims to fame included a folding trigger, two superimposed barrels, and a '2 x 2' breech-block. The two upper chambers were fired sequentially, then the block was rotated laterally through 180° to allow the third and fourth shots to be fired. The Bär-Pistole was reloaded simply by rotating the breech-block to its intermediate 90° position and punching the spent cases out of the chambers with a suitable tool. The first guns were chambered for a special 7mm cartridge, but post-1906 examples accept 6.35 mm Auto rounds instead.

Revolving-cylinder types

The Little All Right was one of the smallest 'squeezer' handguns. Patented in January 1876 by Edward Boardman and Andrew Peavey, and made in Lawrence, Massachusetts, by the Little All Right Fire Arms Company, it was a tiny five-shot .22 rimfire revolver operated by a trigger bar which slid back above the barrel housing. The revolver was held with the vestigial butt against the ball of the thumb, allowing the muzzle to peep through between the index and first fingers. The index finger retracted the trigger-bar, cocking the hammer, rotating the cylinder, and then releasing the hammer to fire the gun.

MULTI-BARREL DESIGNS

Tipping barrels

The break-open derringer patented in May 1857 by William Marston of New York City had a monoblock containing three rifled barrels. The earliest experimental guns had a double-action trigger, which was replaced by a simpler single-action version before series production began. About 1,400 first-pattern .22 rimfire Marston pistols were made in 1858–64; they were 5½in long and had 3in barrels. A few even had short knife blades on the left side of the barrel block. The hammer body was set into the frame, and a combination safety catch/selector lay on the right side of the frame ahead of the hammer. A travelling striker fired the barrels sequentially from the bottom upward.

An improved Marston, introduced in 1864, chambered .32 rim-

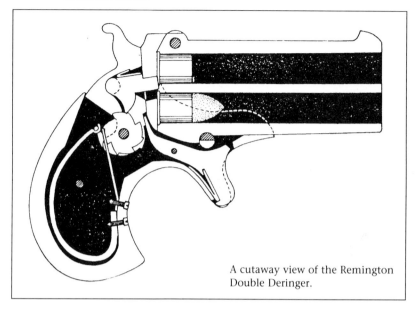

A cutaway view of the Remington Double Deringer.

fire cartridges in a bid to improve performance. An extractor was set into the right side of the frame; the selector was numbered '0', '1', '2' and '3'; and the body of the hammer projected from the frame-back.

Work continued until 1874 in short and long versions, with barrels measuring 3in and 4in respectively.

Patented in 1860–1, the Remington-Elliot derringer had a multi-

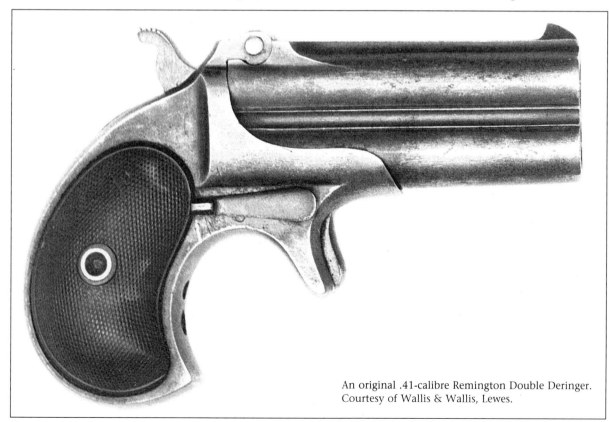

An original .41-calibre Remington Double Deringer. Courtesy of Wallis & Wallis, Lewes.

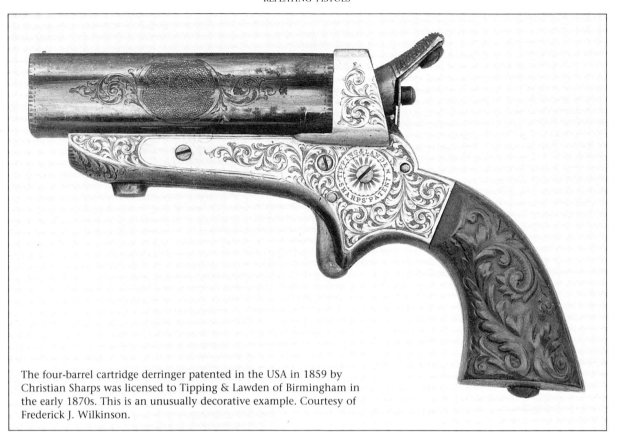

The four-barrel cartridge derringer patented in the USA in 1859 by
Christian Sharps was licensed to Tipping & Lawden of Birmingham in
the early 1870s. This is an unusually decorative example. Courtesy of
Frederick J. Wilkinson.

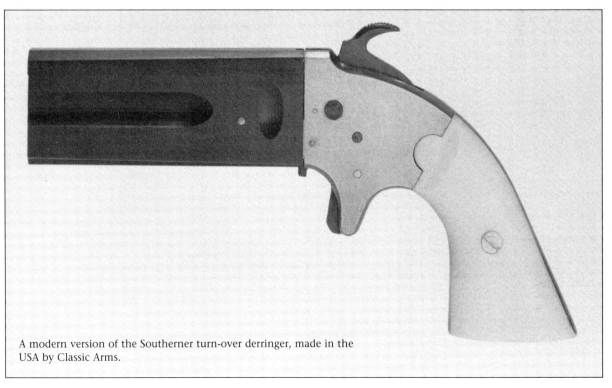

A modern version of the Southerner turn-over derringer, made in the
USA by Classic Arms.

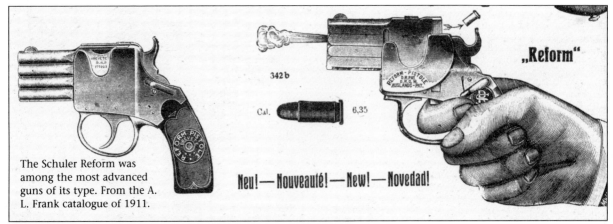

The Schuler Reform was among the most advanced guns of its type. From the A. L. Frank catalogue of 1911.

342b

Cal. 6,35

„Reform"

Neu! — Nouveauté! — New! — Novedad!

shot 3in barrel cluster which tipped down to load. A revolving striker actuated by a ring trigger fired each barrel in turn. The guns were generally blued, but the frames or the entire gun could be nickel-plated to order. Grips were gutta-percha, mother-of-pearl or ivory. About 50,000 five-shot .22 and four-shot .32 derringers were made in 1863–88. Their barrel clusters were cylindrical and squared respectively.

The Remington Repeating Double Deringer (sic), designed by William Elliot, was patented in the USA in December 1865 and introduced commercially in 1866. Sales were amazingly good; when work finally ceased in 1935 about 150,000 had been made. The essential feature was a pair of superimposed 3in .41 rimfire barrels in a monoblock hinged to the frame. The barrel block swung upwards around a pivot at the top rear of the frame when the lever on the right side of the frame was pressed downward, allowing the gun to be reloaded. The firing pin fired the top barrel first, being reset each time the frame was opened.

Few changes were made to the design during its long life, except that an extractor was added in the early 1870s. Most of the guns were nickel-plated, although blued examples were produced in small numbers. Their grips may be walnut, rosewood, chequered gutta-percha, mother-of-pearl or ivory. The guns were about 4¾in long

and weighed 11oz empty. They were marked E. REMINGTON & SONS ILION N.Y. ELLIOTS PATENT. DEC. 12th 1865 until 1888, REMINGTON ARMS CO. ILION N.Y. from 1888 to 1910, and then REMINGTON ARMS – U.M.C. CO. ILION N.Y. until the end of production. Many copies have since been made in recent years, particularly in Italy.

Double Derringers soon became popular in the West, replacing single-shot cap-locks as the favourites of bankers, gamblers and whores alike. A surprisingly discerning clientele was found in the bordellos which traded discreetly in Eastern cities or, flamboyantly, in the 'Hell on Wheels' towns which flourished and died as the railheads pushed on across America. The cap-lock derringers had been liked for the ease with which they could be concealed in a purse or a garter; the Remingtons were excellent replacements, with the bonus of an extra shot. One of the most infamous of the earliest guns was given about 1877 by the gambler and sometime dentist John 'Doc' Holliday to his paramour, 'Big Nose' Kate Elder. The legend *To Kate from Doc* was engraved on the backstrap.

The subject of a patent granted in December 1906 to Oscar Mossberg of Chicopee Falls, the Unique was made for a few years by C. S. Shatuck of Hatfield, Massachusetts. A four-barrel block, fired by a slider-actuated rotary striker, could be tipped down in the blued or nick-

el-plated iron frame to load. Unique pistols accepted .22 or .32 rimfire cartridges. Interest in these guns was strong enough to persuade Cornelius Vanderbilt Jr to patent an improvement in March 1916.

A 6.35mm gun with a four-barrel block, sold under the brandname 'Regnum', was made by August Menz of Suhl from 1910 until the beginning of the First World War. Production is believed to have totalled 1,000. The barrels were locked by a sliding catch on the left side of the frame, immediately ahead of the safety catch, and were fired sequentially. A four-hammer disc on a central spindle struck each of four separate firing pins set in the standing breech. Spent cases were ejected automatically as the breech was opened. Regnum pistols were usually marked D.R.G.M. u. AUS-LANDS-PATENT on the side of the frame, and had an 'AM' monogram moulded into the rubber grips. They were 110mm long, had 67mm barrels and weighed about 360gm empty.

The Tomma was similar to the Menz Regnum, with a tipping four-barrel block, but had a noticeably rounder appearance, a shorter grip, and a simple push-button barrel catch instead of a slider. Though a few 7.65mm examples have been reported, most of the guns accept 6.35mm Auto cartridges. About 3,000 were made in Germany, apparently near Oberndorf, and 2,500 by Manufacture d'Armes 'HDH' in Liége. Proof marks are the most obvious distinguishing feature, but the Belgian-made guns are longer (95mm compared with 87mm) and cruder.

A variation of the tipping-barrel system was offered in pre-1914 A. L. Frank catalogues as the 6.35mm 'Alfa'. This had a top-lever latch and a striker which fired each barrel sequentially, but its origins are still unknown.

Sliding barrels

Christian Sharps made thousands of his distinctive four-barrel derringers between 1859 and 1874, when they were licensed to Tipping & Lawden in Britain and North American production ceased. The sheath-trigger Sharps guns were offered in .22, .30 and .32 rimfire, with barrels of 2½–3¼in. The barrels were arranged as two rows of two, sliding forward to give access to the breech after a catch had been released. A rotating striker-plate ensured that the chambers were fired in the correct order. This was generally fitted on the hammer, but lay in the frame of some Sharps & Hankins guns. Frames were blued iron or brass, often plated with nickel or silver; the grips were walnut, gutta-percha, ivory or mother-of-pearl.

Laterally rotating or 'turnover' barrels

The pedigree of this group dates back to the earliest days of firearms history. Match-, wheel-, flint- and cap-lock versions were made in surprising quantities, particularly in the eighteenth and early nineteenth centuries. Included among these guns were some which were small enough to be pocketable.

The advent of the metal-case cartridge encouraged production of repeating pistols, which were much simpler and easier to make than pepperboxes and revolvers. A typical two-barrel design was registered in Britain in February 1863 by Woodward of Birmingham. It

was a simple sheath-trigger design with a sliding hammer-locking catch on the back strap of the frame. After the first shot had been fired, the barrel cluster was rotated through 180° to fire the second round. The hammer was then retracted to half-cock and the barrels were turned through 90° to give access to the chambers.

A typical Woodward derringer, chambered for a .240 rimfire cartridge, was about 4¾in long and had a 2½in barrel. Similar guns were made by Philip Webley & Son in the late 1860s. However, these were larger and more powerful than their predecessors, chambering a selection of cartridges from 6mm rimfire to .44 rimfire or .450 centre-fire.

The turnover derringer patented in 1865–6 by Henry Wheeler was a simple sheath-trigger design. A two-barrel monoblock rotated through 90° to give access to the breech once a small spring-loaded latch on the underside of the frame had been released. Turning the barrels through 30° conferred a measure of safety. Made from 1867 by the American Nut & Tool Company of Boston, Massachusetts (subsequently renamed 'American Arms Company'), the Wheeler was initially offered in .32 Short and .41 rimfire, and then also in a .22/.32 combination. Operations moved from Boston to Milwaukee in 1893, continuing until the American Arms Company was sold to Marlin in 1901. The barrel lengths of the three patterns were 2½in, 2⅝in and 3in respectively. Some guns were browned, but others were plated with nickel.

The two-barrel derringer designed by Franklin Wesson was introduced in 1868, and an improved version with a flat-sided frame made its debut a year later. Some of the first-pattern pistols (and possibly a few of the improved design) were made with sliding knife blades housed on the left side of the barrel block. The block rotated laterally to the right when the latch protruding beneath

the frame ahead of the sheath trigger was pressed: a particularly poor feature, as the barrel often opened unexpectedly in the confines of a pocket. The Wesson derringers were offered in .22, .32, .38 or .41 rimfire chamberings, the .38 version being by far the least popular. They were 4–6in long, and had barrels of 2–4in.

MOVING-BARREL DESIGNS

Sliding type

Among the most interesting of all repeating pistols was the 'Reform', patented in 1905 by August Schuler of Suhl. About 4,000 are said to have been made by 1914. The distinctive four-barrel block was raised vertically in the frame, shot-by-shot, by a double-action trigger mechanism. Each shot was fired by a single hammer and striker at the height of the first or uppermost barrel when the barrel-block was in its lowest position. Spent cases were expelled by residual propellant gas bled from the firing barrel through connecting ports. The fourth, or lowest case had to be extracted manually after the barrel block was removed for loading. A safety lever lay on the left side of the frame beneath the hammer.

The earliest guns were distinguished by flat-sided frames and BREVETE/D.R.P./177023 on the left side of the barrel block. A later type, possibly made by another contractor, had flat-sided barrels and a frame with prominent curved-bottom fairings. These guns were marked REFORM-PISTOLE, arched over D.R.PAT./D.R.G.M./AUSLANDS-PAT. Grips were marked REFORM-PISTOLE and BREVETE in a roundel, together with an 'SR' (Schuler Reform?) monogram.

Revolving types

About 1,000 .22 rimfire six-shot Zig-Zag derringers, patented in 1858–60 by William Elliot, were made by E. Remington & Sons before the Civil War began.

AUTO-LOADING PISTOLS

The mechanical repeater, which was successful only in its smallest sizes, was rapidly succeeded by the semi-automatic pistol. Experimental work had been undertaken in Spain, Britain and France in 1860-85, but the earliest automatic pistols to be introduced successfully were all German: the Borchardt, the Bergmann and the Feederle-Mauser. However, virtually all of these were intended specifically for military purposes, and were much too large to be readily concealed.

The Bergmann-Schmeisser, patented in Germany in May 1893, was effectively the prototype of the pocket automatics of the twentieth century. The inclusion of a delay element in the earliest breech mechanism meant that the bolt had to be released from contact with a shoulder in the receiver before running back to compress the return spring, but experience showed that this additional complication was unnecessary. Louis Schmeisser reverted to simple blowback operation in subsequent designs.

Bergmann filed another important patent in Germany in 1893 (No. 78,500) to protect a true blowback action. The breech was 'locked' at the instant of firing only

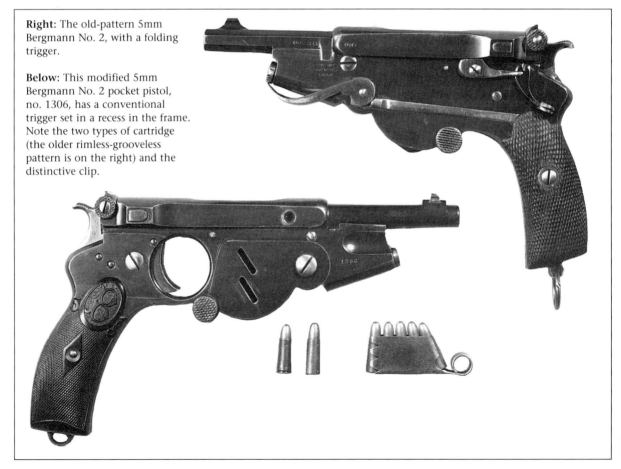

Right: The old-pattern 5mm Bergmann No. 2, with a folding trigger.

Below: This modified 5mm Bergmann No. 2 pocket pistol, no. 1306, has a conventional trigger set in a recess in the frame. Note the two types of cartridge (the older rimless-grooveless pattern is on the right) and the distinctive clip.

by the inertia of the heavy bolt and the pressure of the recoil spring. When the gun was fired, the bolt ran back in the receiver, relying on an extension rod running forward from the breech on the right side of the frame to compress an under-barrel spring. The spur hammer was cocked as the bolt ran backwards, the trigger mechanism was adapted from single-action revolver practice, and a disconnecter prevented fully automatic fire. A transverse bar in the bolt (called the 'crosshead' in the patent specifications) was stopped by the receiver bridge at the limit of the recoil stroke. The return spring then propelled the bolt back to battery, stripping a round from the magazine into the chamber as it did so.

The 1894-type Bergmanns were made in several sizes. The largest, for military use, originally chambered an 8mm round. However, a catalogue of the period states that the design could be adapted to most pistol and revolver cartridges loaded with smokeless powder.

At least one 6.5mm-calibre gun was made in the early 1890s, but a true pocket pistol was shown in the patent drawings. A folding trigger in front of the magazine housing acted on an extension bar (set into the left side of the frame) to rotate the hammer. This little gun chambered a tiny 5mm rimless/grooveless round. At least one pistol in this calibre was supplied to the Swiss in 1894, but surviving records do not state whether it had a folding trigger. A plate on the side of the pistol frame depressed the cartridge-follower arm when swung forward. A clip, usually containing five rounds, was then placed in the magazine well and the side plate was returned to its original position. A small coil

Right: This 5mm Bergmann new-model No. 2 is cased with its accessories, including a magazine clip (middle, far left), a turn-screw and a cleaning rod. Courtesy of Wallis & Wallis, Lewes.

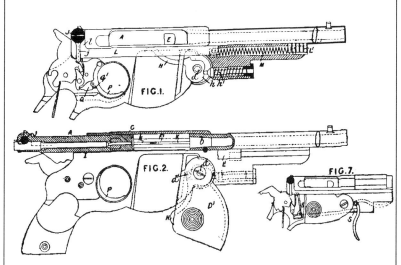

Taken from the British patent granted in 1893, 'Fig. 3' shows the original version of the Bergmann pocket pistol.

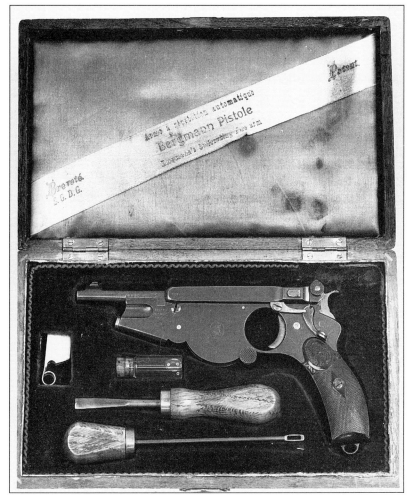

spring under the barrel applied pressure to the follower arm and the cartridge column; when the last cartridge had been chambered, the spent clip fell downward and out of the gun.

The original Bergmann-Schmeisser lacked an ejector. The sharply tapered cases, lacking extractor grooves, were simply blown from the chamber by the residual gas pressure in the breech. Extraction was surprisingly efficient, but ejection depended on the case striking the blade-type ejector accurately. The slightest deviation as the case flew out of the breech created problems. As ejection needed to be approximately vertical for the case to avoid hitting the receiver walls, misdirected cases occasionally failed to clear the feed-way and the returning bolt jammed them (or the new round) against the barrel casing.

By the end of November 1894 Eisenwerke Gaggenau had submitted a selection of Bergmanns for trials in Switzerland: two 8mm, two 7.5mm, one standard and an experimental 6.5mm, and one 5mm. The experimental weapon had a 're-positioned lock spring', protected by German Patent 78,881.

THE PERFECTED BERGMANN PISTOLS

Bergmann-Schmeissers of the new or '1896' pattern appeared on the commercial market in the autumn of 1895. They were very similar to the preceding semi-experimental guns and had a return spring within the breech bolt. The magazine side-plate had two diagonal slots instead of a raised thumb rib, and the safety lever was redesigned to incorporate an external safety-lever spring.

The hinged side-plate magazine was substantially the same as that patented in 1893, accepting a five-round, single-sided pressed steel clip. It has been claimed that the clip could be pulled out to leave the cartridges loose in the feed way, using the loop protrud-

ing from the bottom of the magazine. However, this leaves too much space between the cartridges and the receiver walls, and the gun tends to jam. The clip also holds the cartridges too tightly to make removal practicable; the loop was apparently intended solely as a handling aid.

The first production Bergmanns retained the rimless/ grooveless cartridges, relying simply on residual gas pressure in the chamber to expel spent cases. Only a few guns

of this type, probably no more than 1,500, were sold commercially in 5mm and 6.5mm forms.

Literature published by Eisenwerke Gaggenau about 1896 confirmed the existence of only three basic Bergmann pistols, though others had been made for military tests. The Pistole No. 3 is most common, chambered initially for the 6.5mm rimless/grooveless cartridge and then for its more conventional grooved successor. However, the No. 3, which was about

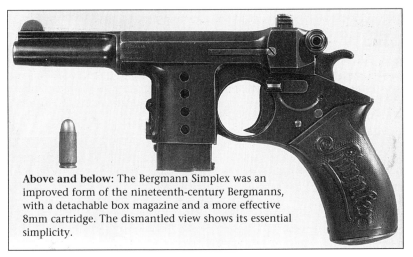

Above and below: The Bergmann Simplex was an improved form of the nineteenth-century Bergmanns, with a detachable box magazine and a more effective 8mm cartridge. The dismantled view shows its essential simplicity.

250mm overall and weighed 850gm unloaded, was too long to be classed as a genuine pocket pistol even though production estimated at about 3,250 guns places this Bergmann among the most successful first-generation automatics.

The guns chambered for the diminutive 5mm round were true pocket pistols, the perfected Bergmann No. 2 being the first successful automatic of its genre. According to Bergmann catalogues, the earliest 5mm No. 1 was only 140mm long, 80mm high and 18mm thick. Its unloaded weight was a mere 300gm. The magazine held five rimless/grooveless rounds, and the barrel and frame were forged in a single piece. Production is assumed to have been very small, as few guns of this type survive.

The 5mm No. 2 is more plentiful. The older pattern, probably dating from 1895–6, fired rimless/grooveless ammunition and had a folding trigger. The barrel lug engaged a recess in the left frame rail, where it was held by a transverse screw. The guns were 175mm long, 110mm high, 22mm thick, and weighed 470gm. Serial numbers apparently ran upward from '1' to about 500. German proof marks – crown/crown 'U' – lay on the left side of barrel and frame, together with '611' (the calibre, 611-Bore) and PATENT/BREVETE/ S.G.D.G. on the frame ahead of the barrel locking-screw head.

The folding-trigger pocket pistol did not prove as popular as Bergmann had hoped. Accidents may have been caused by the unprotected trigger, but the pistol was also expensive and its handling characteristics were undoubtedly inferior to those of the pocket revolvers of the day. Consequently, a revised version of the No. 2 was introduced in the summer of 1896, probably at about the time a conventional extractor was added to the 6.5mm No. 3.

The perfected No. 2 Bergmann had the trigger in an aperture in the frame behind the magazine well. It was slightly longer than its predecessor, though height and thickness were comparable. Overall length was about 195mm, unloaded weight being 550gm. The barrel lug was held by a transverse screw on the left side of the frame above the magazine follower/side-plate pivot. A fixed lanyard loop lay beneath the butt, a large 'B' was moulded into the grips, and the front sight was carried on a raised saddle. The markings duplicated those of the folding-trigger No. 2, with an oval cartouche containing a lamp-carrying miner ('Bergmann' in German) on the left side of the magazine housing. The marks BERGMANN and V.C.S./SUHL also appeared, identifying the manufacturer as V. C. Schilling of Suhl. Serial numbers continued where those of the folding-trigger pattern stopped, doubtless with a limited overlap as old components were expended. The highest reported number is 2177, which suggests that total production amounted to about 1,700.

A small hole drilled through the right side of the frame into the chamber of the perfected No. 2 has attracted several explanations, though the Bergmann manual states quite simply that it '. . . enables [the firer] to ascertain whether there is a cartridge in the barrel . . .' The bright brass case was easily caught by the eye. The port could double as a gas escape, but there is no evidence that Schmeisser ever had this in mind.

The performance of the Bergmann pistols is difficult to ascertain from the meagre evidence. The absence of an extractor from the earliest guns undoubtedly led to extraction/ejection failures, but these were corrected by adding a conventional extractor. One 6.5mm pistol tried in Britain in 1902 was fired 50 times as rapidly as possible, but did not jam at all.

The military-pattern Bergmann pistols made to the patents of 1893–7 were not efficient enough to withstand the challenge of the Luger, the Mauser C/96 and the FN-Brownings, and disappeared early in the twentieth century. This was partly due to the loss of the vital manufacturing facilities — Schilling withdrew after being acquired by Sempert & Krieghoff — but the obsolescence of the basic designs also played a part.

A modified version of the basic blowback pistol was made in the early 1900s as the 8mm Bergmann-Simplex, which had a detachable box magazine. A few thousand may have been made in Germany, though not by Schilling. It is often claimed that the guns were made in Liége, but they invariably bear German proof marks and one of the lesser

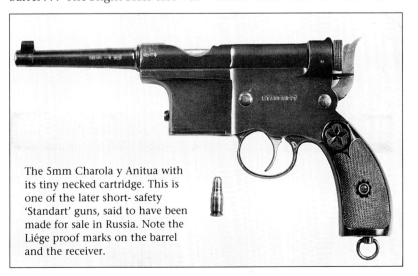

The 5mm Charola y Anitua with its tiny necked cartridge. This is one of the later short- safety 'Standart' guns, said to have been made for sale in Russia. Note the Liége proof marks on the barrel and the receiver.

Thuringian gunmakers was probably responsible. Manufacturing quality was not particularly good. The frame was comparatively soft, the one-piece rubber grip was fragile, and the extractor and ejector were both prone to fracture.

THE CHAROLA Y ANITUA

Among the earliest pistols worthy of mention is this Spanish example, which is said to have been designed in 1895. If this can be proven, the Charola y Anitua demands recognition as one of the first successful small-calibre automatics. It was patented in Spain in 1897 by Ignacio Charola, a gunmaker of Eibar, and marketed with the assistance of businessman Gregorio Anitua.

The Charola pistols had a locked breech and a box magazine ahead of the trigger, and bore a superficial resemblance to the Mauser C/96. The earliest were about 235mm long, had 104mm barrels and weighed about 850gm. Distinctive features included revolver-like lines, particularly in the vicinity of the trigger, and the extended safety lever on the rear left side of the frame. Markings included PISTOLA AUTOMATICA PATENTE CHAROLA Y ANITUA EIBAR on top of the barrel, and a winged-bullet trademark on the left side of the frame above the trigger. The bullet was accompanied by a scroll displaying either MARCA REGISTDA or TRADE MARK. The Charola y Anitua was originally chambered for a small 5mm cartridge, which was scarcely powerful enough to justify the wedge-type breech lock. A 7mm version was introduced by DWM about 1900.

The first guns were made in Spain by, or possibly for, Charola y Anitua. They were not particularly successful, owing to the parlous state of Spanish metallurgy, and components may subsequently have been purchased from Belgium. The identity of the manufacturer is not known.

Charola y Anitua pistols were scarcely pocketable, but about 5,000 seem to have been made when production ceased about 1904. The 5mm guns were more common than the 7mm type, but the greatest legacy was the smaller of the two cartridges, popularised in Belgium and central Europe in later years as the '5mm Clément'.

THE FIRST BROWNINGS

Although Theodor Bergmann and Louis Schmeisser had been the first to market simple blowback pistols in quantity, the guns were not successful enough to revolutionise the compact semi-automatic. This was due largely to the genius of John Moses Browning of Ogden, Utah.

Browning had constructed a prototype blowback in the mid-1890s, chambering a .32 semi-rimmed cartridge made by Winchester. The pistol was successfully demonstrated to representatives of Colt in the summer of 1895, and a patent application was filed in September. The granting of the patent was delayed until the spring of 1897, but, even before the printed specification had been published by the US Patent Office, Browning had refined the original design by replacing its distinctive internal bolt and hinge-crank recoil unit with a simple bolt carried inside a full-length slide. This slide had been shown on US Patent 580,926, application for which had been filed in the USA in October 1896. Only one pistol of this type is known to have been made. It was delivered to Colt in May 1896, together with a recoil-operated pattern locked by dropping the barrel on two swinging links and a third gun locked by rotating the barrel.

Doubting the virtues of small calibre and the absence of a breech-lock, Colt decided that no suitable domestic market existed for the blowback pistol. Rights immediately reverted to the inventor. Early in 1897, however, Hart Berg, the commercial manager of Fabrique Nationale d'Armes de Guerre (FN), was sent to the USA to review improvements being made in the manufacture of bicycles.

During his travels in North America, Berg was introduced to the Browning family. John Browning casually remarked that, though he was pleased with the designs being exploited by Winchester and Colt, he was still seeking a licensee for patents protecting the blowback pistol. Berg agreed to approach the FN administrative council as soon as he returned to Europe, and an agreement was signed with Browning on 17 July by the president of Fabrique Nationale, Baron Charles de Marmol.

Although many months elapsed before production methods had been perfected (the first guns were not made in Belgium until 1898), the superiority of the perfected Browning blowback pistol was soon evident. The basic design was one of five designs protected by British Patent 9,871 of 1897, four of which were the work of John Browning and the fifth (a quirky blow-forward pistol) by Carl Ehbets. Browning and Fabrique Nationale sought improvements, and in 1898 requested more protection in several European countries.

Records retained by FN indicate that nearly 4,000 Browning pistols were made in 1899. Except for a handful of pre-production guns, these were all similar to the perfected 1900 model. However, they were 183mm overall instead of 162mm, and weighed 765gm compared with 625gm. Their frames were noticeably plainer than the later type, the grips were much smaller, and there was no lanyard ring.

The Belgian army adopted the FN-Browning blowback in July 1900, making it one of the first semi-automatics to be accepted for military service. The guns also proved to be attractive commercial propositions.

THE 1900-TYPE FN-BROWNING

This was the first comparatively small automatic to be made on a large scale. Fabrique Nationale made the 100,000th 1900-type gun in August 1904, half a million had been made by 1909, and produc-

Above and below: The 1900-pattern FN-Browning was the first auto-loading pistol to be made in truly large numbers, production exceeding a half-million by 1907. Originally intended for military service, many guns were instead sold commercially. These included highly decorated examples. Courtesy of FN Herstal SA.

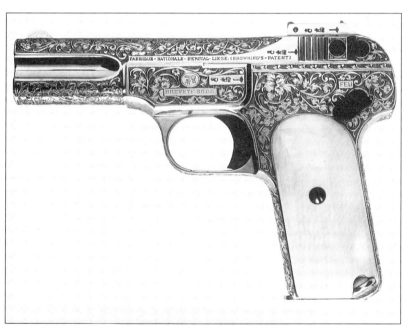

government guarantee') was also struck into a raised panel milled out of the left side of the frame. Liége proof marks were standard.

A notable enlargement of the milled side panels soon occurred, apparently to strengthen the frame. Instead of running back as far as the mid-point of the trigger-guard bow, they reach the rear of the guard itself. The grips were enlarged, five broad slide-retracting grooves replaced six narrow ones, and the head of the small safety lever was chequered instead of concentrically ribbed. A lanyard ring generally appeared on the lower left side of the butt. The markings on the left side of the slide became FABRIQUE NATIONALE D'ARMES de GUERRE HERSTAL BELGIQUE above the FN monogram/pistol cartouche, which was stamped into a raised panel on the left side of the frame above BROWNING'S-PATENT/BREVETE S.G.D.G.

A catalogue distributed in 1905–6 by Manufacture Française d'Armes et Cycles of Saint-Étienne offered the standard 1900-pattern FN-Browning for 45 francs; lightly engraved overall for 60 francs; with pearl grips for 70 francs; and engraved and inlaid, 'Modèle de Luxe', for 100 francs. Each gun was supplied with a screwdriver, a cleaning rod and three dummy cartridges. By comparison, the Old Model Luger cost 110 francs in France in this period. A box of 25 7.65mm cartridges made by Société Française de Munitions (SFM) cost 2 francs 75, spare magazines were 2 francs 50, and two types of case were available: 'toile grenat, satin' or 'beau cuir, velours' (red cloth covering with a satin lining, or plush-lined leather).

THE EARLIEST AMERICAN AUTOMATICS

The year 1903 was marked by the introduction of .32 and .38 Colt Pocket Models. The .32 gun was an adaptation of the contemporary 7.65mm 1903 'Grand Modèle' FN-Brownings, developed to persuade European governments that

tion ceased in 1911 at gun no. 724,450. This impressive total aptly illustrates the impact of the Browning blowbacks on the pre-1914 gunmaking industry. More than any other single design, they were responsible for the eclipse of the European-made pocket revolver.

The earliest FN-Brownings were marked FABRIQUE NATIONALE HERSTAL LIEGE in a single line on the left side of the slide, immediately above a small cartouche containing a pistol and a cursive FN monogram. The latter, together with BREVETE S.G.D.G. (*Sans Garantie du Gouvernement*, 'without blowbacks could be acceptable militarily. A detachable barrel was held inside the full-length slide by ribs beneath the chamber engaging a block on the frame, a return spring lay beneath the barrel, and an enclosed hammer was fitted.

The subject of a US patent granted to Browning in December 1903, the finalised .32 Colt was smaller and lighter than its Belgian prototype and lacked the lanyard loop on the butt. Marketed commercially from the summer of 1903, the Colt had a 4in barrel (reduced to 3¾in when a .380 version appeared in 1908), an eight-round magazine and weighed 23–24oz. The moulded rubber grips generally displayed COLT and the rampant colt motif.

More than 10,000 .32-calibre guns were sold in the first year of production. Most were blued, though nickel plating was popular and engraved versions could be supplied to order. Except for changes in the slide legend, modifications to the slide-retracting grooves made in 1905–6 and the

elimination of the barrel bush in 1910, no changes were made to the Colt during its production life; 572,215 had been made when the .32 was finally discontinued at the end of the Second World War.

The Colt .38 Pocket Model, introduced in the autumn of 1903, was simply a short-barrelled Sporting Model – a locked-breech Browning – with a round hammer and conventional slide-retracting grooves above the moulded grips. The form of the grooves changed perceptibly in 1908, when they became deeper and closer together, and a spur hammer superseded a rounded pattern in the same era. The .38 locked-breech Pocket Model was discontinued in 1929 after about 22,000 had been made. It was superseded by the blowback .380 Pocket Model of 1909. This chambered a rimless cartridge developed by Browning in collusion with William Thomas of the Union Metallic Cartridge Company. Apart from calibre marks, the .380 was virtually identical with the original .32 Hammerless Pocket

Model. The extractor was modified to suit .32 or .380 guns interchangeably, and the magazine capacity was reduced from eight to seven rounds. The barrel bush was eliminated in 1910, shortening slides and barrels by a quarter of an inch. The .380 pistol was not as successful as the .32 version, and only about 138,000 had been made when work was abandoned in 1946.

THE POCKET BROWNINGS

The 1903-pattern FN-Browning was primarily intended as a military and police weapon, though substantial numbers were sold commercially. It also laid the basis for the world's first truly successful pocket-size automatic. The 'Pistolet Browning, Calibre de 6,35mm' was patented in Belgium in 1905.

Often known unofficially as the 'Model 1906', the Browning was introduced commercially in 1907. Resembling a diminutive M1903 externally, it had a shorter slide and a truncated butt. The grip safety was retained, a safety lever lay

The 1903-pattern FN-Browning blowback pistol, intended for military service, was too large to be considered as pocketable, though some assassins managed to prove otherwise. This particular presentation gun was inlaid in gold and fitted with mother-of-pearl grips. Courtesy of FN Herstal SA.

on the left rear of the frame, and the magazine catch was under the heel of the butt. There was scarcely enough space in the tiny frame for a hammer, so a striker mechanism was substituted.

These guns were made in huge quantities, though nothing like the 'four million' that has often been claimed. Work finally ceased when the Germans invaded Belgium in 1940, after 1,080,000 had been made. According to the A. L. Frank catalogue, the basic 6.35mm FN-Browning was selling in Germany in 1911 for 53.20 marks. A nickel-plated version with rubber grips was 55.53 marks, and an engraved nickelled example, with pearl grips, cost 93.53 marks. Spare magazines cost 2 marks apiece. The guns were customarily delivered in a cardboard box containing a magazine full of dummy cartridges and a cleaning rod. Most 6.35mm FN-Brownings are marked FABRIQUE NATIONALE D'ARMES de GUERRE HERSTAL BELGIQUE above BROWNING'S PATENT DEPOSE on the left side of the frame, the left side of the slide, and the top of the barrel. The hard rubber grips bear the company monogram.

Colt's .25-calibre Hammerless Pocket Pistol was a variation of the 6.35mm Browning, the production line being readied at the Hartford factory in 1907 with the assistance of Fabrique Nationale. Prototypes retained an internal hammer, but experience showed that this was too difficult to fit into so small a gun, and a duplicate of the FN striker mechanism (with an additional manual safety) was substituted. The extractor was fitted externally, and a magazine-release catch lay under the butt. Moulded rubber grips invariably displayed COLT and the rampant colt motif. Production began in 1908, and when work stopped in 1941 nearly 410,000 guns had been made. Patents granted to Arthur Wright in August 1896 were acknowledged in addition to Browning's, even though nothing of the abortive Wright pistol was used. The manu-

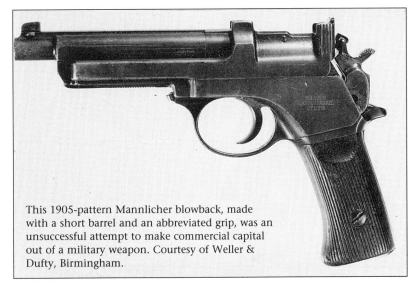

This 1905-pattern Mannlicher blowback, made with a short barrel and an abbreviated grip, was an unsuccessful attempt to make commercial capital out of a military weapon. Courtesy of Weller & Dufty, Birmingham.

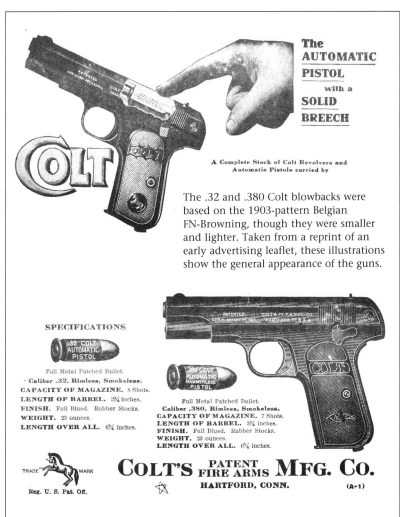

The .32 and .380 Colt blowbacks were based on the 1903-pattern Belgian FN-Browning, though they were smaller and lighter. Taken from a reprint of an early advertising leaflet, these illustrations show the general appearance of the guns.

al safety, which could lock the sear or hold the slide open, was patented by Browning in January 1910. Pistols made after 1916, when numbers had reached 141000, incorporated an additional magazine safety patented on behalf of George Tansley in July 1917.

AUTOMATIC PISTOLS
AND THE LAW

The advent of mass-produced automatic pistols coincided with a sudden rise in political assassinations, and the first decade of the twentieth century was a catalogue of horror. After an unsuccessful attempt on the lives of King Edward VII and Queen Alexandra in Brussels in April 1900, King Umberto of Italy was shot dead in July 1900, US President William McKinley died as the result of an assassin's gunshot in September 1901, King Alexander and Queen Draga of Serbia were murdered in Belgrade in June 1903, Grand Duke Sergei (uncle of Tsar Nikolai II) was killed in St Petersburg in February 1905, Greek premier Delyannis was shot in Athens in June 1905, and Bulgarian premier Nikolai Petkov died in March 1907. February 1908 brought the deaths of King Carlos I and Crown Prince Luiz of Portugal.

Unsuccessful attempts had also been made on a wide range of public figures, ranging from the premiers of France and Russia to the kings of Belgium and Spain. Anarchists were blamed for most of these incidents, often favouring the bomb over the gun. However, as several attacks had involved revolvers, the introduction of compact automatic pistols – which were more powerful than revolvers of comparable size – raised great public concern. Tsar Nikolai II is said to have armed his personal bodyguards with the tiny 6.35mm FN-Brownings immediately they appeared on the market.

Britain was one of the first countries to restrict the distribution of handguns, though the pioneering Pistols Act of 1903 may be seen more as a surreptitious source of

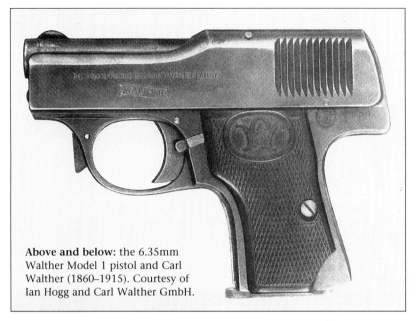

Above and below: the 6.35mm Walther Model 1 pistol and Carl Walther (1860–1915). Courtesy of Ian Hogg and Carl Walther GmbH.

revenue than truly effective legislation. Control was restricted to pistols with barrels measuring less than 9in (about 23cm), and faint hearted attempts were made to ensure that guns could not be used by 'incompetents'.

No more successful was a law passed in Austria-Hungary in 1909 to prevent the sale, without express permission, of guns measuring less than 18cm (7in) overall. Perpetuated in Czechoslovakia until 1939, this was intended to restrict the use of short-barrel guns to government servants. Gunmakers were forced to solve the problem in different ways. Some simply extended barrel sleeves without altering the barrel itself; the Walther Model 1 is an example of this approach. Others provided special components. The Steyr and Clément pistols had long barrels forged integrally with the recoil-spring guides. Extending a barrel shroud or lengthening an otherwise standard barrel was the most popular solution. It allowed purchasers to buy guns which conformed with the letter of the law, then modify them simply by shortening the barrel. Some manufacturers helpfully mounted front sights well back from the muzzle to facilitate alteration.

THE RISE OF COMPETITION
The runaway success of the FN-Brownings could hardly have passed unnoticed in the Liége area, where gunsmiths worked together, drank together, fought together, and competed for a share of a market dominated by the personal-defence revolver. When the pistols began to threaten sales of all but the cheapest and most primitive revolvers, many men strove to compete with FN. The earliest rivals, based loosely on the 1900-pattern FN-Browning, were exemplified by the first Clément,

and Jieffeco pistols made by Janssen, fils et Cie. The introduction of the 6.35mm Browning, however, diverted interest to small-calibre pocket weapons. Belgium briefly became the centre of automatic-pistol production, but the heyday ended with the German invasion in 1914.

A major problem was posed by the Browning patents, which prevented copies of the 6.35mm FN-made pistol being marketed until after the First World War in virtually every European country except Spain, where foreign patents went unrecognised until the 1920s. The guns that reached production status before 1914, therefore, often incorporated distinctive features. Some were too complicated for their size; others were simply too fragile to survive hard use.

The 6.35mm-calibre FN-Browning was the first auto-loader to offer truly compact dimensions. Its overall length was about 114mm, which FN regarded as the minimum acceptable size for a handgun. However, though FN was satisfied with its pocket pistol, rival manufacturers sought to save the few millimetres that would allow them to claim that their guns were the smallest on the market. The

first to make a feature of compact dimensions seems to have been Carl Walther of Zella St Blasii, when the first 6.35mm Model 2 Walthers appeared on the market in 1913. Walther claimed the magic figure of 10cm (3.9in), though this had been deftly rounded-down from the true length of about 106mm.

Among the most interesting of Belgian guns of this period were the Clément and the Pieper. Details of others will be found on page 97.

IMPROVED FN-BROWNINGS
By 1908, FN had realised that the basic Browning-type blowback could be improved; competition demanded a new design if the company was to retain its pre-eminence. The Model 1910 FN-Browning, patented in Belgium in July 1909, was destined to become another outstanding success. In its external appearance and internal construction it differed considerably from its predecessors. The return-spring assembly (above the barrel of the 1900 pattern, beneath in the 1906 type) was superseded by a coil spring concentric with the barrel. A special bushing held in the front of the slide by a bayonet joint pushed the spring against the

Right: The 6.35mm FN-Browning was not only the first truly pocketable semi-automatic pistol, but also a great trend-setter. Courtesy of FN Herstal SA.

barrel shoulder as the slide ran back. The 1906-type striker and trigger mechanism were retained, modified to smoothen movement and shorten lock time. Grip and manual safeties were supplemented by a new magazine safety, always a feature of questionable utility in a defensive weapon.

The pistol was among the neatest and most elegant designs of its day. Its calibre could be changed from 7.65mm to 9mm simply by replacing the barrel, the recoil spring and the magazine. As the gun was very easy to dismantle, and as the barrels were retained in the frame only by simple transverse ribs, a change could be accomplished in seconds.

Markings included FABRIQUE NATIONALE D'ARMES de GUERRE. HERSTAL - BELGIQUE above BROWNING'S - PATENT DEPOSE. in two lines on the left side of the slide. Liége proof marks were standard, and the calibre mark (e.g., CAL 7m/m65) also appeared. The FN monogram was moulded into the plastic grips.

The slide mark was changed in the 1920s to FABRIQUE NATIONALE D'ARMES DE GUERRE S.A. HERSTAL BELGIQUE above an acknowledgement of the patent, with the upper line running virtually the entire length of the slide from the muzzle to the retraction grooves. This style was soon replaced by a narrower version, stopping some way short of the grooves.

The Model 1910, later known simply as 'Model 10', remained in production until 1940 and then reappeared in the 1950s in a modernised form. Browning & Gentry, writing in *John M. Browning. American Gunmaker*, report sales of 572,590 M1910 and Model 10 pistols by 1961, but this is difficult to reconcile with FN's claim to have sold a million by 1936.

MORE BROWNING RIVALS

The success of the Browning blowbacks made by FN and Colt, notably the minuscule .25 ACP/6.35mm pocket pistol, per-

The 1909-pattern Pieper, shown here in a 7.65mm version made in the Steyr factory (proved in Austria in 1910), was also available as a 6.35mm pocket pistol. Courtesy of Ian Hogg.

suaded many other manufacturers to compete. The Belgians were the earliest market leaders, as the Germans had been slow to realise that a market existed for anything other than powerful military auto-loaders. Theodor Bergmann had shown an inclination to make smaller guns, but had retired from the firearms-making business when Schilling, his principal subcontractor, had been purchased in 1904 by Krieghoff.

Most of the small-calibre pistols designed in Germany emanated from the traditional gunmaking districts in Thuringia, centred on the town of Suhl and the adjoining villages of Mehlis and Zella St Blasii. The Adler was one such design.

The interesting dismantling system and enclosed breech-block of the Adler were patented in Germany in August 1905, the essentially similar British Patent, 14,023/06, following in October 1906. Both record the name of the patentee as Max Hermsdorff. The British papers go farther, describing him as 'trading as Adlerwaffenwerk Zella St. Bl., of 12 Hammerweg, Zella St. Bl., Germany.' References in the markings on the guns to Haeussler and Engelbrecht & Wolff give no clue to their significance. Hermsdorff has been con-

nected with patents assigned in the pre-1914 era to Krupp, but who was Haeussler? The partnership of Engelbrecht & Wolff is also shadowy; did it succeed Hermsdorff, or were the Adler pistols simply made under subcontract? Unless satisfactory information is found in Suhl, the answers may never be known.

The origins of the 7mm Adler cartridge seem to lie in the 7mm Charola y Anitua pattern, introduced by Deutsche Waffen- und Munitionsfabriken in the early 1900s for the Spanish pistol of the same name. Adler rounds were made exclusively by Rheinische Metallwaaren- und Maschinenfabrik of Sömmerda and invariably headstamped 'R☆M☆S'.

The Adler bears some external resemblance to the Luger, with a slender barrel, a raked grip and pronounced backward overhang. The barrel screws into the receiver. The only visible motion on firing is the cocking spur, which reciprocates on top of the receiver. The pistol was cocked by retracting the spur against the pressure of the return spring until the striker mechanism engaged. Releasing the cocking piece at the end of the backward stroke allowed the breech block to run forward, chambering a new round as it did so.

The patented dismantling system was controlled by unlocking the uppermost pin in the rear of the frame and then rotating the frame-closing link around the lower pivot. The breech block, the main spring, and the spring guide could then be removed; the drawings accompanying the patent specifications show this feature clearly. The trigger had to operate a lateral sear, a feature clearly inspired by the Luger. But instead of using a pivoting bellcrank, the designer of the Adler used a trigger bar with a diagonal cam surface bearing on the sear piece. The action was probably not robust enough to function efficiently. The trigger and the sear were too delicate, and there were far too many springs.

The guns were marked PATENT HAEUSSLER on the right side of the receiver, above ADLERWAFFENWERKE and ENGELBRECHT & WOLFF over a distinctive trademark depicting a displayed eagle, clasping a riband in its talons, above an encircled 'MHZ'. The trademark is also moulded into the chequered rubber grips; it clearly indicates Max Hermsdorff, Zella St. Blasii. Only a small quantity of guns, perhaps no more than a few hundred, were made prior to about 1908. Overtaken by more efficient designs, the Adler would probably have enjoyed greater success if it had chambered a more popular cartridge.

The failure of pistols such as the Adler and the Keszler to satisfy the German market, where the FN-Browning had gained pre-eminence, inspired Carl Walther, his eldest son Fritz and cousin Friedrich Pickert to begin work on a gun of their own. A few 6.35mm-calibre 'Venus-Pistolen', also called the 'Original-Venus-Pistole' after the slide marking, were made in 1907–8, together with a handful of 7.65mm examples and, perhaps, a 9mm prototype or two.

The pistol had a distinct affinity with the popular Model 1900 FN-Browning, with the recoil spring in a separate chamber above the barrel. Characteristic slide-guides were placed high on the side of the frame, the retraction grooves covered much of the narrow portion of the slide above the grip, and a safety lever lay on the left side of the frame. Except for the position of the slide-retraction grooves, the Venus-Pistole was a thoroughly conventional striker-fired blowback. It measured about 120mm overall, had a 55mm barrel, and weighed 330gm unloaded. The detachable box magazine held seven rounds.

Only a few hundred Venus pistols were made before the advent of the improved 1910-pattern Walther. The illustration in Pollard's book *Automatic Pistols* suggests that they were marked ORIGINAL-"VENUS"-PISTOLE on the left side of the slide and 'Carl Walther WAFFENFABRIK Zella St. Blasii' on the right. The illustration also suggests that the grips, probably rubber or composition, bore a 'CW' monogram.

The failure of the Venus-Pistole forced the Walthers to reconsider their design. A new blowback pocket pistol had been introduced commercially by 1911, being featured in the ALFA catalogue of the period. Walther's sales literature has often claimed origins as early as 1908, and others have dated them as early as 1906; the gun was not patented in Germany until November 1911, however, and the '1908' factory date was nothing more than a clumsy attempt to gain prestige at the expense of Mauser.

The earliest examples of the 1910-type Walther, simply marked D.R.G.M., were made before the patent had been granted. The Model 1910 had been renamed 'Model 1' by 1913, owing to the introduction of the Model 2. The slide of the Walther Model 1 did not entirely envelop the barrel, which was contained in the three-quarter-length annular jacket that screwed into the standing frame. When the pistol was fired, the slide compressed the return spring beneath the stationary barrel against the barrel-block on the frame. An unusual transverse safety catch lay in the frame behind the grips.

Prior to 1912 the Walthers had been dismantled by locking the slide in its retracted position with a small catch on the front of the trigger guard. The barrel jacket could then be unscrewed and detached. The slide was pulled backward, lifted to disengage the slide rails, and then allowed to run forward and off the frame. The slide, recoil spring and recoil-spring guide all came away from the frame together. In later guns, from no. 15001 to the end of production at about 31200, the slide was returned to its rest position once the barrel jacket had been removed. The catch on the right rear of the frame was pressed inward and the slide was pulled back for about half an inch, then lifted from the frame rails before being allowed to run forward. The striker and striker spring could be removed from the interior of the slide.

The Model 1 was needlessly complicated, difficult to machine and more expensive than its rivals. It was replaced in 1913 by the Model 2.

The first pistols were apparently marked WALTHER'S SELBSTLADE-PISTOLE CAL. 6,35 above D.R.G.M. IN- & AUSLANDSPATENTE ANG. on the left side of the slide, showing clearly that patents had been sought (but not then granted) in Germany and abroad. Fifteen retraction grooves were milled vertically into the slide, and the grips generally bore 'CW' monograms. The slide inscription changed once the patent had been granted, thereafter reading SELBSTLADE-PISTOLE CAL. 6,35 above "PATENT" on the left side, with WALTHER'S PATENT on the right side of the frame above the safety catch.

The advent of the new dismantling catch was accompanied by a change in the slide retraction grooves, which were widened to improve grip and reduced from fifteen to twelve. The contours of the frame behind the trigger were straightened, and the slide inscrip-

Above and below: The perfected 1910-model FN-Browning blowback pistol was an outstanding success before the First World War. These photographs capture its elegant lines. Courtesy of FN Herstal SA.

tion changed to SELBSTLADE-PIS-TOLE. CAL. 6,35. WALTHER'S PATENT over the now-familiar banner trademark.

Although annual sales were exceeding 10,000, the Walther Model 1 had clearly failed to challenge the dominance of the FN-Brownings. Development of the basic ideas allowed the simplified Model 2 to reach the commercial market in 1914, though much of Walther's sales literature dated this gun to 1909. Patent legislation shows this claim to be unduly optimistic.

Makers of Pocket Automatic Pistols, 1905-18

NOTE: unless stated otherwise, the guns all chamber 6.35mm Browning (.25 ACP) cartridges.

Martin A. Bascaran, Eibar, Spain
Martian, Thunder.
Beistegui Hermanos, Eibar, Spain
Bulwark.
Établissements Bernardon, Martin & Cie., Saint-Étienne, France
Bernardon-Martin, 'Hermetic'.
Manufacture Générale d'Armes et Munitions Jules Bertrand, Liége, Belgium
Le Rapide.
Fabrique d'Armes Charlier & Cie, Liége, Belgium
Wegria-Charlier or 'WS'.
Charles Ph. Clément, Liége, Belgium
Models of 1907, 1908, 1909 and 1912.
Colt's Patent Fire Arms Manufacturing Co., Hartford, Connecticut, USA
Hammerless Pocket Model.
Fabrique d'Armes F. Delu & Cie, Liége, Belgium
Fabrique Nationale d'Armes de Guerre, Herstal-lèz-Liége, Belgium
Modèle de Poche, or 'Model 1906'.
Fegyver és Gépgyár Részvénytarsaság, Budapest, Hungary
Frommer 'Baby' (also in 7.65mm and 9mm Short).
Auguste Francotte & Cie, Liége, Belgium
Harrington & Richardson Arms Co., Worcester, Massachusetts, USA
Hammerless Model.

Société d'Armes HDH (Henrion, Dassy & Heuschen), Liége, Belgium
'H&D'.
Jules Jacquemart & Cie, Liége, Belgium
Le Monobloc.
Janssen, Fils & Cie, Liége, Belgium
Jieffeco.
Friedrich Langenhan, Suhl, Germany
FL Model 3.
Österreichische Waffenfabriks-Gesellschaft, Steyr, Austria
Model 1909.
Anciens Établissements Pieper SA, Herstal-lèz-Liége, Belgium
Bayard.
Phoenix Arms Company, Lowell, Massachusetts, USA
Fabrique d'Armes N. Pieper, Liége, Belgium
Models 'C' ('Demontant'), 'P' ('Basculant'), 'D', and 1909 (also in 7.65mm).
Fabrique d'Armes Réunies, Liége, Belgium
Centaure, Dictator.
Rheinische Metallwaaren- u. Maschinenfabrik, Sömmerda, Germany
Dreyse.
Carl Walther, Zella St Blasii, Germany
Models 1, 2, 3 (7.65mm) and 5.
L. & J. Warnant Frères, Hognée, Belgium
Webley & Scott Ltd, Birmingham, England
Hammerless Pocket Model, Pocket Model.

US-MADE BROWNING RIVALS

Sensing a growing market, a few American pistol manufacturers were willing to compete with Colt, even though challenging the popularity of the small-calibre double-action revolver must have seemed daunting. The announcement of the US Army pistol trials of 1906 led to the submission of auto-loading pistols of American design. The best known was the .45-calibre Savage, originally patented by Elbert Searle of Philadelphia in November 1905. Guns improved in accordance with an additional patent sought in January 1907 (but granted only in 1909) were submitted to the US

Army by the Savage Arms Company. They put up a creditable showing and were accepted for field trials once the Luger had been withdrawn.

Savage also made a .32-calibre personal defence pistol incorporating the same locking system and parts which interlocked without screws. The first gun was assembled in the company's Utica factory on 22 March 1908, chambering the '.32 ASP' (Automatic Savage Pistol) cartridge, a minor variant of the popular .32 ACP or 7.65mm Auto. The slides were marked MANUFACTURED BY THE SAVAGE ARMS CO. above UTICA. N.Y. U.S.A. PAT– NOV. 21. 1905 ahead of CAL. .32.

The 1907-type Savages were about 6½in long, had 4in barrels and weighed about 19oz without their ten-round magazines. The unusually large capacity allowed the advertising slogan 'Ten Shots Quick' to be coined. The guns had moulded plastic grips and a round hammer protruding from the top of the slide, though a spur-type hammer was substituted after 1919. The retraction grooves were originally very broad, but a narrow pattern was soon substituted. The original ridged safety was exchanged at the beginning of 1909 for a chequered-head design, but this was superseded in 1912 by a special pattern amalgamated with a Lang Patent trigger-lock bar. The magazine-release catch in the front of the butt was altered in the middle of 1912, and a loaded-chamber indicator, patented on behalf of Charles Nelson in December 1913, was added shortly afterward.

The modified 1915-type .32 Savage appeared when serial numbers had reached about 130000. It had a concealed hammer and a grip safety system patented by William Swartz. The standard slide legend was changed in this period to SAVAGE ARMS CO. UTICA. N.Y. U.S.A. CAL. .32 above PATENTED NOVEMBER 21. 1905–7.65. M-M. Marks of this type were retained until 1920, when 'Savage Arms Corp.' replaced 'Savage Arms Co.' in the upper line.

The basic exposed-hammer pattern was not discontinued until April 1920, shortly after the refined M1917 had been introduced. Production amounted to about 208,800, making the .32 Savages second only to Colt on the North American market.

Savage made a large .380 version of the Model 1907 from May 1913 onward, but these were usually regarded as holster pistols rather than to be concealed for close-range defence. Their numbers began at B2000, the prefix becoming a suffix after a few hundred had been made. The .380 Savage was abandoned in 1920 after little more than 15,000 had been made.

A hammerless .25 blowback Savage was developed about 1914, but the commencement of war-work prevented its exploitation. Attempts were made to revive the project in 1919, but the ready availability of war-surplus handguns dissuaded Savage from the risk. Only about 100 .25 guns were made, in two subvarieties. They had 2⅜in barrels and weighed about 12oz without the six-round magazine. Magazine safeties were standard.

Harrington & Richardson made Webley-inspired self-loading pistols, refinements being patented in the USA in 1907 and 1909. Production was painfully small; despite their excellent quality, the guns were too expensive to compete with the small Colts and only about 17,000 guns were made. The .25 H&R pattern was manufactured only in 1912–15, though the .32 version, with an additional grip safety, lasted from 1916 until 1940.

Smith & Wesson elected to compete with Colt by making a variant of the Belgian Clement, patented in the USA in September 1910. Joseph Wesson added a grip safety and a disconnector for the recoil spring, patented in 1910

and 1912 respectively, and the first seven-shot 3½in barrelled guns were assembled in May 1913. They chambered a unique .35 cartridge, loaded with a bullet with a half-jacket of cupro-nickel over a protruding lead core. The magazine catch was altered to work longitudinally early in 1914, but few other major changes were ever made. Sales were initially quite brisk, but production stopped in April 1915 to concentrate on war-work for Britain. Work resumed in the summer of 1916, only to stop again at the beginning of 1918. When the pistol was finally put back into production, in February 1919, the markets were flooded with war surplus. The last of only about 8,000 .35 Smith & Wessons was completed in July 1922.

SPANISH BROWNING COPIES
The success of the 6.35mm Browning pocket pistol was much greater than FN had predicted. Demand soon outstripped supply, allowing enterprising entrepreneurs to market a wide range of similar-looking rivals. Browning patents were still binding in Belgium until the First World War, however, preventing copies being made in Liége.

The situation was entirely different in Spain. The indigenous gunmaking industry, chartered by Philip II in 1562, was centred on the northerly part of the country. Most gunmakers operated in the province of Viscaya, in and around the towns of Eibar, Ermua and Guernica. They also had links with associates in Bayonne and Hendaye in the Basque region of south-western France.

The relationship of the Basques with their fellow countrymen was traditionally uneasy. Although the gunmakers were often able metalworkers, therefore, their industry was starved of capital and military contracts were customarily fulfilled in government-sponsored factories in other regions. Spanish gunsmiths lacked nothing in skill,

producing an automatic revolver as early as 1863, but the advance towards industrialisation was slow. Output in the nineteenth century was surprisingly high, comparing favourably with that of Birmingham and Liége, but the advent of machinery allowed companies such as Fabrique Nationale to undertake mass production. Gunmaking in Spain remained on a cottage-industry basis.

The Spaniards were still handicapped by a shortage of modern machinery in 1914, when many smaller 'manufacturers' (little more than assemblers or finishers) were still buying their forgings from a handful of metalsmiths until the unexpected bonanza provided by the First World War.

Spanish gunmaking was neither fettered by mandatory proof nor bound to recognise foreign patents until the 1920s, unless they had first been sought in Spain. As patents were divided into several classes, including registered designs and trademarks, the country remained a copyists' haven for many years.

Locked-breech pistols were unpopular in Spain in the early twentieth century, as they were difficult to make satisfactorily. The failure of the promising Charola y Anitua to establish a market turned attention to simpler designs. The elegant blowback Mannlicher was copied by Garate, Anitua y Compañía of Eibar, with two important changes; the 7.65mm Auto cartridge was substituted for proprietary Austrian ammunition, and a detachable box magazine replaced the original charger-loading type. The magazine was even curved to follow the line of the grip. These guns were sold as 'La Lira' and 'Triumph'. Most were too large to be carried comfortably in a pocket, but a few short-barrelled and short-gripped examples were also made.

The most fertile source of inspiration was the 6.35mm FN-Browning pocket pistol. From 1906 until 1912, the Spanish derivations were characterised by some originality. Typical of these were the Star, introduced by Julio Echeverria in 1906–7, and the original Garate, Anitua y Compañía 'Express'. Both of these simple blowbacks resembled minuscule Mannlichers externally. The Express was a particularly interesting gun, with an open-top slide and a barrel with a top rib. The left side of the frame was marked THE BEST AUTOMATIC PISTOL »EXPRESS« and the safety markings were usually in French.

The Mondial by Gaspar Arizaga, offered in 6.35mm and 7.65mm, was outwardly modelled on the 1907-pattern Savage. Internally, however, it was an ordinary blowback. The No. 1 had grip, magazine and manual safety systems, but was rapidly replaced by the simpler No. 2 with manual safety only.

Francisco Arizmendi's Boltun, dating from about 1910, was based on the Belgian Pieper. It lacked the tipping barrel of the prototype, but still relied on a separate bolt reciprocating within the frame. Marks were confined to AUTOMATIC PISTOL above BOLTUN PATENT on the left side of the barrel block; safety markings were often in French. The original 6.35mm Fiel, made in Eibar by Erquiaga, Muguruzu y Compañía, was another distinctive gun with a tubular bolt. When the Fiel was fired, the bolt compressed the return spring against a shoulder in the rear of the frame.

Virtually all of these guns except the Star were soon replaced by simpler Browning-type 'Eibar' guns. Indeed, most of 6.35mm pistols made in Spain after 1912 were modelled directly on the original FN pattern. Some were virtually indistinguishable copies, but most had a characteristic feature – the design and location of the manual safety catch in the frame above the trigger. A hammer mechanism was usually substituted for the striker, and the grip was sometimes lengthened to increase capacity.

Said to have been made for sale in Finland, this 6.35mm Joha is typical of the Spanish-made Browning copies. Courtesy of Ian Hogg.

Makers of Spanish Pocket Pistols

The details given here are confined to copies and adaptations of the FN-Brownings which are less than 127mm (5in) overall, have short butts, and could be regarded as pocketable. Many gunsmiths made otherwise identical guns with their butts elongated to accept magazines of nine, ten or even twelve rounds. Without exception, the pistols chamber the 6.35mm or 7.65mm Auto or Browning cartridges (.25 and .32 ACP).

Acha Hermanos y Compañía, Ermua
  Atlas, Ermua, Looking Glass.
Aguirre, Zamacolas y Compañía, Eibar
  Basculant, Le Dragon.
A. Aldazabal, Eibar
  'AAA'.
Hijos de José Aldazabal, Eibar
  Imperial.
Fábrica de Armas Alkartasuna SA, Eibar
  Alkar.
Apaolozo Hermanos, Eibar (and/or Zumárraga?)
  Paramount, Triomphe.
Gaspar Arizaga, Eibar
  Pinkerton.
Francisco Arizmendi, Eibar
  Boltun, Kaba Spezial, Le Pistolet Automatique, Roland, Singer, Victor, Ydeal.

F. Arizmendi y Goenaga, Eibar
  Teuf-Teuf, Waldman, Walman.
Armero Especialistas, Eibar
  Omega.
Eulogio Arostegui, Eibar
  Azul, 'E.A.'.
Hijos de Calixto Arrizabalaga, Eibar
  Terrible.
Azanza y Arrizabalaga, Eibar
  Reims.
Azpiri y Compañía, Eibar
  Avion, Colon.
Martin A. Bascaran, Eibar
  Martian, Thunder.
Victor Bernedo y Compañía, Eibar
  'B.C.', Bernedo.
Bersaluce Arietio-Aurtena y Compañía, Eibar
  Allies.
Beistegui Hermanos, Eibar
  'B.H.', Bulwark, Libia.
Gregorio Bolumburu, Eibar
  Bufalo, Gloria, Marina, Regent, Regina, Rex.
Crucelegui Hermanos, Eibar
  Campeón, 'C.H.', Crucelegui.
Manufactura de Armas 'Demon', Eibar
  Demon.
Echave y Arizmendi, Eibar
  Bronco, Lightning, Protector, Renard, Selecta.
Hijos de A. Echeverria, Eibar
  Vesta.
Erquiaga, Muguruzu y Compañía, Eibar

Diane, Fiel, Marte.

Antonio Errasti, Eibar
Errasti.

Fabrica de Armas Automaticas 'E.S.A.', Eibar

Esperanza y Unceta, Guernica
Astra, Fortuna, Union, Victoria, Vite.

Fábrique d'Armes de Grande Précision (Extezarraga y Abitua), Eibar
Ca-Si, Colonial, Grande Précision, Helvece, Jubala, Jupiter, Minerva, Precision, Princeps, Trust.

Gabilondo y Compañía, Elgoeibar
Danton, Veritable Mosser Superior.

Gabilondo y Urresti, Elgoeibar
Bufalo, Perfect, Radium, Ruby Arms Co., Tauler.

Garate Hermanos, Ermua
Cantabria.

Garate, Anitua y Compañía, Eibar
Sprinter, Vesta.

Isidro Gaztañaga, Eibar

Guisasola Hermanos, Eibar
Guisasola.

Lasagabaster Hermanos, Eibar
Douglas.

Ojanguren y Vidosa, Eibar
Apache, Puppel, Salvaje, Tanque.

Orbea y Compañía, Eibar
Orbea.

Orbea Hermanos, Eibar
La Industrial.

F. Ormachea, Eibar
Duan, Merke.

D. F. Ortega de Seija, Madrid
Benemerita.

Retolaza Hermanos, Eibar
Gallus, Liberty, Military, Retolaza, Stosel, Titan, Titanic.

Santiago Salaberrin, Eibar
Etna, Protector, Tisan.

Iraola Salaverria y Compañía, Eibar
Destructor.

Casimir Santos, Eibar
El Cid, Venzedor.

Modesto Santos, Eibar
Action, 'MS',

Sociedad Española de Armas y Municiones (SEAM), Eibar
Diana, Praga, 'S.E.A.M.', Sivispacem, Waco.

Thieme y Edeler, Eibar
Sivispacem Parabellum.

Unceta y Compañía, Guernica
Firecat, Union, Unique, Victoria.

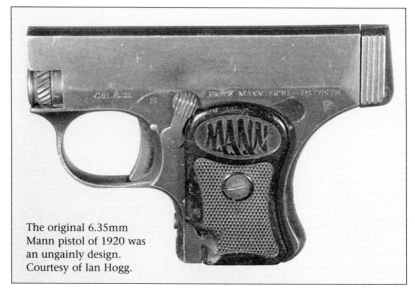

The original 6.35mm Mann pistol of 1920 was an ungainly design. Courtesy of Ian Hogg.

Fábrica de Armas 'Union', Eibar
Rival.

Unknown and unattributed
Asiatic, Aurora, Automatic Pistol, Cow Boy, Defense, Dewaf, Favorit, Handy, Hudson, Joha, Olympia, Radium, Rayon, Tatra, Tiwa, Vulcain, Zaldun.

Tómas de Urizar, Barcelona
Celta, Continental, Ermua, Express, J. Cesar, Le Dragon, Le Secours, Phoenix, Premier, Princeps, Principe, Puma, Venus.

M. Zulaica y Compañía, Eibar
Royal, The Victory, Vincitor.

BETWEEN THE WARS

Few gunmakers found the years immediately after the end of the First World War anything but barren. Demand for guns had been diminished by a pervading anti-war mood, or by the tremendous quantities of war-surplus weaponry.

Few real advances were made in handgun design in 1918–25, even though the race to market the smallest practicable auto-loading personal defence pistol began again with surprising vigour.

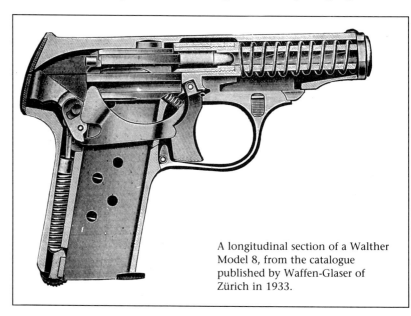

A longitudinal section of a Walther Model 8, from the catalogue published by Waffen-Glaser of Zürich in 1933.

Shortly after the First World War, Austrian gunsmith Franz Pfannl made a surprising number of Erika pistols, an idiosyncratic design chambered for a 4.25mm cartridge. Said to have been designed in 1914 around a cartridge developed by Hirtenberg Patronenfabrik, the Erika was a simple blowback with a curious box magazine in the frame between the trigger guard and the grip. It was 100mm long, had a 42mm barrel and weighed 260gm without the magazine. Although the gun undoubtedly worked efficiently, its ammunition was far too weak to be an effective deterrent, and work ceased in the late 1920s.

Pfannl had also made pistols for Georg Gräbner, a wholesaler of sporting goods based in Rehberg bei Krems an der Donau. The result of this collaboration was the Kolibri, a diminutive Erika just 65mm long with a 30mm barrel and an unloaded weight of about 220gm. The Kolibri is the smallest semi-automatic pistol ever to be marketed, by a wide margin. It chambered tiny 2mm (earlier) and 3mm (later) cartridges, and was much too small to be anything other than a toy even though it undoubtedly held some threat at very short range.

One of the first 6.35mm guns to be offered was made by Fritz Mann of Suhl. The unusual but oddly proportioned Mann pistols (advertised as the models of 1920 and 1921) had a bolt reciprocating within the frame instead of the customary detachable slide. However, the grip was much too short to give a good grip and the bolt often pinched the web of the thumb when it ran back on firing. Sales were too meagre to justify continuing work, and in 1924 Mann switched to a conventional slide-and-frame 7.65mm gun.

The end of the First World War gave many gunsmiths the chance to reappraise their products. The first tangible result of the work of Fritz Walther was the Model 8, patented in 1920 but only marketed once the approval of the Allied supervising commission had been sought. The first pistols appeared commercially in 1922. The Model 8 bore a superficial external resemblance to the 1910-type FN-Browning, though the guns were quite different internally. However, though the Model 8 proved to be a popular replacement for the wartime Model 7, it was accompanied by a much more influential 'shirt-pocket' pistol superseding Models 1, 2 and 5. This Model 9 was destined to be made in greater numbers than any other pre-1929 Walther.

The construction of the Model 9 was patented in Britain in April 1921, allowing the pistol to reach the commercial market in 1922. The guns were striker fired and had a slide design adapted from that of the pre-war Model 1. This did not completely envelop the barrel, being cut away for much of its length. The return spring lay beneath the barrel, where it was compressed against the standing frame when the gun was fired. The barrel construction typified the earlier Walthers, being a thin annular sleeve within a barrel housing forged integrally with the frame. The safety catch thumb-piece was attached to an extension bar which protruded from the top front of the left grip;

101

when pushed down to cover the letter 'F', exposing the upper 'S', the safety-catch spindle revolved to lock the sear. The magazine release catch lay on the heel of the butt.

The Model 9 introduced yet another patented dismantling system. After ensuring that the gun was empty, the bottom lip of the magazine was used to press inward on a small spring-loaded catch which protruded from the rear of the frame beneath the slide. This allowed the striker anchor (shaped like a dumb-bell) to move backward about 8mm and out of the frame. Assembly was simply the same process in reverse. The slide was replaced and pushed down at the rear, then the striker anchorage was pressed back until it was locked by the spring catch. The magazine release catch lay on the heel of the butt.

The Model 9 was merely 101mm overall, had a 50mm barrel and weighed 255gm without its detachable six-round box magazine. Slides were marked *Walther's Patent. Mod. 9* on the left side, above the company's banner trademark, with *Waffenfabrik Walther Zella-Mehlis (Thür.)* on the right. The earliest slides had concealed extractors and eighteen retraction grooves, milled slightly diagonally.

Production seems to have begun at about gun no. 420001. By 445000, however, an external extractor was being used. The grips on pistols made prior to *c*.1927 were composition, with cloisonné enamel inlays, but were replaced by moulded banner-trademark grips held by a single transverse screw set in steel washers. By 1939 the standard pistol, often called the 'Modell 9a', was offered in blued-steel finish with the standard screw-and-washer grips. The deluxe 'Modell 9b' had rolled-in line 'engraving' around the slide legend and powder-blue cloisonné enamel grip motifs. Special '9b' finishes included nickel plating, gilding or heat blueing. Arabesque, floral or oakleaf decoration could be

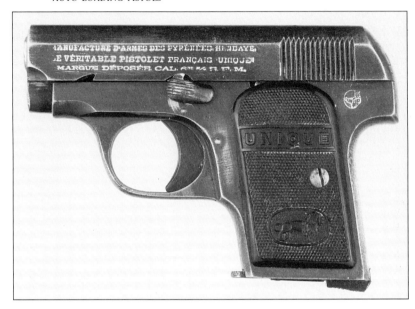

An exploded view of the FN-Browning Baby pocket pistol. Courtesy of FN Herstal SA.

Left and right: Three typical pocket pistols of the inter-war period. **Left:** the French Unique, probably made in Spain. **Right:** Deluxe version of the FN-Browning 'Baby'. **Lower right:** The Czechoslovakian Dusek 'Duo'.

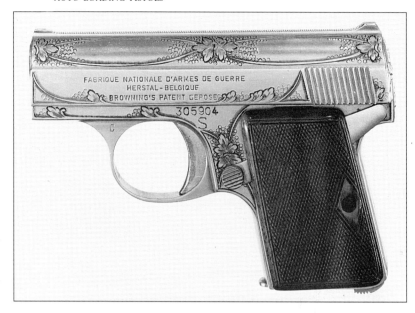

applied to order; grips were usually pearl or ivorine.

According to pre-1939 catalogues, the standard blued Model 9 cost 27.50 Reichsmarks, while engraved and gilded pistols were 98 Reichsmarks. Between 1922 and the termination of production in 1940, at least 280,000 of these tiny Model 9 Walthers were made. Their serial numbers were eventually separated from the other Walthers at about 750000 and continued independently from 100001N.

The Walther pocket-pistol design was very successful, inspiring competitors such as the FN-Browning 'Baby', the Mauser Westentaschen-Pistole ('WTP') and Sauer's Westen-Taschen-Modell.

Among Germany's most ardent champions of minuscule designs was August Menz, who produced the first of his Liliput series in the early 1920s. The earliest Menz Liliputs included one version chambering the 4.25mm Erika cartridge, possibly intended as a sales gimmick, and a larger pattern handling the well-established 6.35mm Auto round.

Many other German manufacturers produced pocket pistols in the 1920s. Among the smallest were the Helfricht Model 4 and the Haenel Model 2. Several Spanish gunmaking companies also produced diminutives of their regular 6.35mm pocket pistols, including Bonifacio Echeverria (Star Model E) and Sociedad de Armas y Municiones Españolas ('SEAM').

Pocket Automatic Pistol Manufacturers, 1918–39

NOTE: owing to uncertainty over dating and attribution, the Spanish-made Browning copies have been listed separately. All guns chamber the 6.35mm Auto (.25 ACP) cartridge unless otherwise stated.

Acha Hermanos, Eibar, Spain
Looking Glass.
Gaspar Arizaga, Eibar
Mondial.
Francisco Arizmendi, Eibar
Boltun.
Eulogio Arostegui, Eibar
Azul.
Karl Bauer, Berlin
Kaba Spezial.
Pietro Beretta SpA, Gardone Val Trompia, Italy

Model 1919.
Theodor Bergmanns Erben, Gaggenau, Germany
Models 2 and 3. Also made as 'Einhand' one-hand cockers (Models 2A, 3A).
Victor Bernedo y Compañía, Eibar
Ceskoslovenske Statní Zbrojovka AS, Brno, Czechoslovakia
CSZ. Later guns were marked 'Ceskoslovenská Zbrojovka'.
Ceskoslovenska Zbrojovka AS, Brno, Czechoslovakia
Vz. 36.
Fabrique Nationale d'Armes de

TREU ABER...

trotz allen seinen guten Eigenschaften als Wächter, hat er eine kleine Vorliebe für das Fleisch und ein vergiftetes Klösschen beraubt Sie schnell eines Verteidigers.

Aus Vorsicht, haben Sie stets bei der Hand eine Browning Pistole. Das ist der sicherste Beschützer Ihres Schlafes. Keine Versager mit dieser Waffe; dank ihrer Form und ihrer grossen Handlichkeit ermöglicht sie ein genaues Zielen. Ausserdem machen ihre drei Sicherungen jedes unbeabsichtigte Losgehen des Schusses unmöglich.

Die automatische Browning Pistole wird ausschliesslich von der **FABRIQUE NATIONALE D'ARMES DE GUERRE** IN HERSTAL BEI-LÜTTICH, BELGIEN, hergestellt, welche bis heute mehr als dritthalb Millionen Stück auf den Markt gebracht hat.

Sichern Sie Ihre Verteidigung mit der automatischen Browning Pistole.

Hourat & Vie, Pau, France
 'H-V'.
Jihoceska Zbrojovka, Prague, Czechoslovakia
 Fox, 1921 and 1922 models.
Theodor Kommer, Zella-Mehlis, Germany
 Kommer Models 1–3.
A. Krauser, Zella-Mehlis, Germany
 Helfricht Models 2–4, Helkra.
AG Lignose, Berlin, Germany
 Models 2 and 3. Also made as 'Einhand' one-hand cockers (Models 2A and 3A).
Fritz Mann, Suhl, Germany
 Models 1920 and 1921.
Manufacture d'Armes Automatiques, Saint-Étienne, France
 Le Steph, Securitas (authentication lacking).
Manufacture d'Armes de Bayonne, Bayonne, France
 MAB, Models A and B, Defender.
Manufacture d'Armes de Pyrénées Françaises, Hendaye, France ('Unique')
 Audax, EBAC, Gallia, Helepco, Kitu, Le Majestic, Lepco, Le Sans Pareil, Mikros, Triomphe Française, Unique Model 10.
Manufacture Française d'Armes et Cycles, Saint-Étienne, France
 Le Français Modèle de Poche, Manufrance.
Ernest & François Mayor, Lausanne, Switzerland
 Arquebusier.
Waffenfabrik Mauser AG, Oberndorf am Neckar, Germany
 WTP Models 1 and 2.
August Menz, Suhl, Germany
 Liliput (4.25mm, 6.35mm), Menta, Model 2, Vest-Pocket.
Fabryka Nakulski, Gneizno, Poland
 Smok.
Ojanguren y Vidosa, Eibar, Spain
 Tanque.
Orbea y Compañía, Eibar, Spain
Österreichische Waffenfabriks-Anstalt, Vienna, Austria
 ÖWA.
Franz Pfannl, Krems an der Donau, Austria

Guerre, Herstal-lèz-Liége, Belgium.
 FN-Browning 'Baby'.
F. Delu & Co., Liége, Belgium.
Frantisek Dusek, Opocno, Czechoslovakia
 Duo, Ideal, Jaga, Perla.
Bonifacio Echeverria, Eibar, Spain
 1906, 1908, 1919 and 1920 patterns, Star Model E.
Erquiaga, Muguruzu y Compañía, Eibar, Spain
 Fiel.
Fémáru-Fegyver és Gépgyár R.T.,

Budapest, Hungary
 Frommer 'Liliput'.
Industria Armi Galesi, Collobeato/Brescia, Italy
 Models 1920, 1923, Model 1930.
Gustav Genschow & Co. AG, Suhl and Berlin, Germany
 Gecado.
C. G. Haenel, Suhl, Germany
 Schmeisser Models 1 and 2.
C. E. Heinzelmann, Plochingen am Neckar, Germany
 Heim.

Erika (4.25mm), Kolibri (2mm, 3mm).

Anciens Établissements Pieper SA, Herstal-lèz-Liége, Belgium
Bayard.

Fabrique d'Armes N. Pieper, Liége
Legia, Model 1920, Modèle de Poche.

Posumávska Zbrojovka, Kdyne, Czechoslovakia (formerly Kohout & Spol.)
Mars, PZK.

Zbrojovka Praga, Prague and Vrsovice, Czechoslovakia
Praga.

Rheinische Waffen- u. Munitionsfabriken, Köln, Germany
Continental.

Manufacture Liégeoise d'Armes à Feu Robar & Co., Liége, Belgium
Melior Model 1, 'M.L.'

J. P. Sauer & Sohn, Suhl, Germany
WTM Models 1925 and 1928.

Schweizerische Industrie- Gesellschaft, Neuhausen am Rheinfalls, Switzerland
Chylewski.

M. Seytre, Saint-Étienne, France
Union or 'Union-France'.

Simson & Co., Suhl, Germany
Models 1922 and 1927.

Sociedad Española de Armas y Municiones, Eibar, Spain
SEAM.

Société d'Armes, Paris, France

Steyr-Daimler-Puch AG, Steyr, Austria
Model 1934. May be marked by

Steyr-Solothurn AG, Solothurn, Switzerland.

Franz Stock, Berlin, Germany

Alois Tomiska, Pilsen, Czechoslovakia
Fox, Little Tom.

Tula Ordnance Factory, Tula, Russia (USSR)
TK.

Unceta y Compañía, Guernica, Spain
Victoria.

Tómas de Urizar, Barcelona, Spain
Continental, Express.

Manufacture d'Armes Verney-Carron & Cie., Saint-Étienne, France
Ver-Car.

A. Vilimec, Kdyne, Czechoslovakia
Slavia.

Albin Wahl, Zella-Mehlis, Germany
Stern.

Carl Walther, Zella St Blasii and Zella-Mehlis, Germany
Model 9.

Wiener Waffenfabrik, Vienna, Austria
Little Tom.

Emil Zehner, Zella St Blasii and Zella-Mehlis, Germany
Zehna.

Safety considerations were paramount in pocket-pistol design. The guns were often used by people who were utterly unfamiliar with firearms, and thus had to be made as safe as they could possibly be to avoid accidents. Automatic or 'grip'

safety levers were fitted to even the smallest and cheapest of the guns made between the wars, when a surge of interest in magazine safety systems was also notable. These prevented the gun firing if the magazine had been removed.

The classical single-action autoloading pistol required both hands to prepare it for action, which was a major disadvantage compared with the utility of double-action revolvers.

One of the experimental .45 White-Merrill pistols submitted to the US Army trials in 1906 had a cocking spur beneath the trigger guard, enabling the shooter to retract the slide with the fingers of the firing hand. Unfortunately, this required too much effort to be acceptable; one-hand cocking was better suited to blowback personal-defence pistols.

One of the first of these was patented posthumously in 1912 on behalf of the Norwegian Ole Krag. The front portion of the trigger guard could slide back in grooves cut in the frame, automatically retracting the slide and cocking the firing mechanism. Releasing the cocking block allowed the return spring to close the breech, stripping a new round from the magazine into the chamber as it did so.

Experience showed that this sliding-block method could be employed in pocket pistols with comparatively weak return springs. Guns of this type, patented by Witold Chylewski, were made in 1919–20 by Schweizerische Industrie-Gesellschaft and thereafter by Theodor Bergmann of Suhl under the brandname 'Einhand' ('One hand'). These were marked THEODOR BERGMANN GAGGENAU above WAFFENFABRIK SUHL–CAL. 6.35–D.R.Pa. Later Bergmann-type pistols bear the marks of Lignose, the upper line of the slide-mark reading AKT.-GES. LIGNOSE. BERLIN.

These 6.35mm-calibre pocket pistols all relied on a sliding trigger-guard block, with a suitably

A 6.35mm Lignose Model 2A Einhand. Courtesy of Ian Hogg.

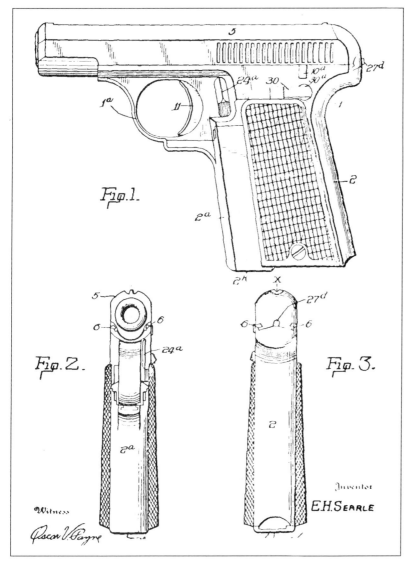

Fig.1.

Fig.2.

Fig.3.

Witness

Inventor

E.H.Searle

Left: Granted to Elbert Searle in November 1921, US Patent 1,395,455 protected a one-hand cocking system for an adaptation of the Savage pistol. Courtesy of the Patent Office Library.

Right: An advertisement for Lignose 'Einhand' pistols, from the Waffen-Glaser catalogue of 1933.

could be fired either by thumb-cocking the hammer or simply by pulling through on the trigger lever for the first shot was a landmark in the history of the personal-defence pistol. The credit is often misleadingly given to Fritz Walther, but surprisingly efficient double-action trigger systems had been applied to cap-lock pepperboxes and revolvers in the nineteenth century – Adams, Allen, Cooper, Remington, Starr and other designs had seen service in the Crimea and the American Civil War – and many major manufacturers had successfully marketed double-action metallic-cartridge revolvers before 1914.

Developing a suitable trigger system for auto-loading pistols was much more difficult, owing to the violence of the action and the strain imposed on their parts. Sergey Korovin and Alois Tomiska had both developed suitable systems prior to 1914, but neither inventor has ever been given much recognition. Korovin, in particular, deserves far greater credit than he customarily receives merely for the single-action 6.35mm TK pistol introduced in the Soviet Union in 1926.

Sergey Korovin was expelled from the Kharkov institute of technology in 1905 'for revolutionary activity', and fled to Belgium at the age of 21. There he worked for the state ordnance factory, Fabrique d'Armes de l'État, and filed the first of his patent applications in Belgium in 1909. British Patent 25,744/12, sought in November 1912 from Rue Grandgagnage, Liége, notes Korovin's declared profession simply as 'Engineer'.

recurved face, to retract the slide. The system was surprisingly resurrected in the People's Republic of China in the 1970s, though the cocking block of the 6.35mm Type 77 pistol has a flat-fronted spur. The Chinese gun also has a fluted chamber to ease extraction problems.

The Spaniard José de Lopez Arnaiz favoured a different approach with his pistol. The earliest Sharpshooter or Jo-Lo-Ar, patented in Spain in 1917, had a sheathed trigger and a barrel which could be tipped up at the breech to load. Opening the barrel was simply a matter of rotating the safety catch past the 'safe' position. An extractor was added in 1919 (spent-gas ejection had previously been favoured) and a pivoting cocking lever appeared on the right side of the slide from c.1923 onward. The Jo-Lo-Ar was usually a substantial weapon, chambering 7.65 or 9mm ammunition, but a compact 6.35mm version could be classed almost as pocketable. Hijos de Calixto Arrizabalaga of Eibar seems to have made them until the 1930s.

DEVELOPMENT OF THE DOUBLE-ACTION TRIGGER

The introduction of a commercially-successful trigger system which

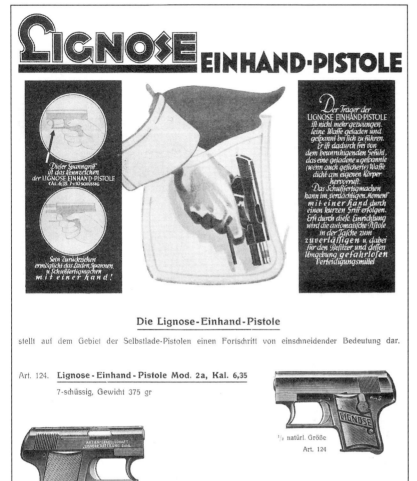

Die Lignose-Einhand-Pistole

stellt auf dem Gebiet der Selbstlade-Pistolen einen Fortschritt von einschneidender Bedeutung dar.

Art. 124. **Lignose - Einhand - Pistole Mod. 2a, Kal. 6,35**

7-schüssig, Gewicht 375 gr

¹/₂ natürl. Größe
Art. 124

¹/₂ natürl. Größe
Art. 125

Art. 125. **Lignose - Einhand - Pistole Mod. 3a, Kal. 6,35**

10-schüssig, langer Griff, Gewicht 415 gr

Reserve - Magazine zu allen automatischen Pistolen jederzeit einzeln ab Lager lieferbar.

tion port when the slide was forward. No guns of this type have yet been found, though it is assumed that at least one working model would have been made. By 1912 Tomiska was declaring himself 'Works Manager' (or *Geschaftsleiter*) of Wiener Waffenfabriks-GmbH, trading in Vienna, where a few large recoil-operated locked breech pistols were made in accordance with patents granted in 1912–13. These were probably created to attract military interest, but work was deferred by the First World War.

The first blowback pocket pistols appeared soon after hostilities had ended, proof marks on surviving guns all being dated in the 1920s. By this time Tomiska had established workshops in Pilsen in newly-emergent Czechoslovakia, and the two patterns were advertised simultaneously under the name 'Little Tom', an Anglicised version of the inventor's name. It is possible, however, that they were all made in the same factory. The 6.35mm Little Tom was a mere 115mm overall, with a 60mm barrel, and weighed about 365gm without its detachable six-round magazine. The six-shot 7.65mm Auto version was 140mm long, had a 78mm barrel and weighed 575–590gm. Its magazine generally held eight rounds, but some short-butt six-round examples may also have been made.

The slides of the earliest guns were marked simply WIENER WAFFENFABRIK above PATENT, with 'Little Tom' moulded into the composition or plastic grips. Later examples, probably made from 1922 until the mid-1930s, were marked WIENER WAFFENFABRIK. PATENT. LITTLE TOM. CAL. 6,35m/m (.25) [or '7,65m/m (.32)']. A distinctive 'WWF' monogram was moulded into the plastic grips or stamped into a medallion set into wood. Guns marketed in Czechoslovakia were marked ALOIS TOMISKA. PLZEN. PATENT LITTLE TOM 6,35 mm (.25), but are scarcer than the Aus-

The patent protected a small blowback pistol with an enclosed hammer and a double-action trigger mechanism, but very little progress was made even though prototypes were tested.

Korovin returned to Russia at the beginning of the First World War, but was unable to find employment as a gun designer until after the Revolution. Appointed to the Tula ordnance factory in 1920, he was able to perfect his double-action pistol, a 7.65mm example being tried by the Red Army in 1923. The tests were successful enough for 50 Korovins to be made in Tula in

1926–7, but the competing Prilutskiy pistol was preferred.

Although Korovin may be due much of the credit for perfecting the double-action auto-loader, there is little doubt that the Bohemian Alois Tomiska was responsible for the first commercially successful design. A British patent application lodged in June 1908 gave an address in Modling, near Vienna, and Tomiska's declared profession as 'Gun Maker'. The blowback-type pocket pistol had an external hammer, a double-action trigger mechanism, and a distinctive plate on the right side of the breech to cover the ejec-

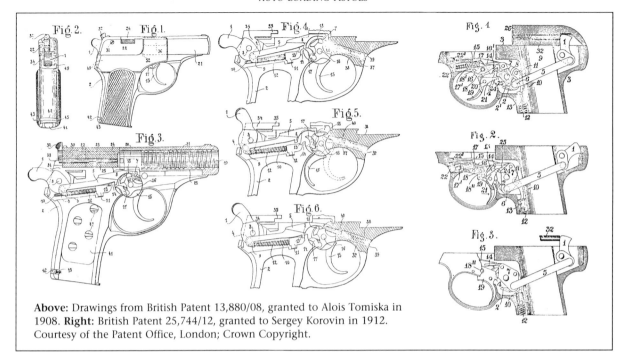

Above: Drawings from British Patent 13,880/08, granted to Alois Tomiska in 1908. **Right:** British Patent 25,744/12, granted to Sergey Korovin in 1912. Courtesy of the Patent Office, London; Crown Copyright.

trian patterns and rarely seen in 7.65mm.

Possibly no more than 20,000 Little Toms were made, but this was sufficient not only to attain a good reputation but also to attract Fritz Walther. The German inventor approached Tomiska in 1922. After acquiring rights to the Bohemian's patents, however,

Walther either deliberately stalled until 1929, when the patents expired through non-renewal, or laboured unsuccessfully for several years to adapt the Little Tom to German mass-production methods. Walther eventually amalgamated the best of Tomiska's ideas with some of his own, and approached the German authori-

ties to obtain an appropriate patent.

THE POLIZEI-PISTOLE

The introduction of this gun, generally known by the abbreviation 'PP', revolutionised the design of personal-defence pistols in a market which had previously been dominated by Browning blowbacks made by Fabrique Nationale d'Armes de Guerre, Colt, and a legion of Spanish copyists.

The new Walther was the first mass-produced auto-loading pistol to compete satisfactorily with double-action personal-defence revolvers, as it could be carried in a pocket with a round in the chamber. All that was needed was to draw the gun, release the safety catch and pull through on the trigger to fire the first shot. It was even possible to carry the Walther in reasonable safety with the safety catch off. Although a pull on the trigger would fire the gun, the length of travel and the force required made accidental discharge unlikely.

Known to the factory as the 'Selbstlade-Pistole Modell 1930', after the year of its first commer-

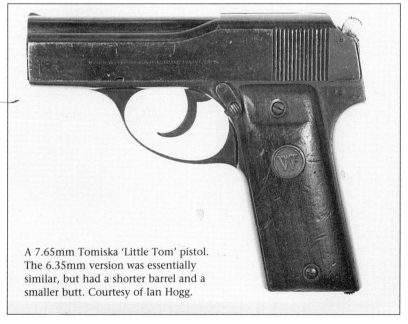

A 7.65mm Tomiska 'Little Tom' pistol. The 6.35mm version was essentially similar, but had a shorter barrel and a smaller butt. Courtesy of Ian Hogg.

cial appearance, the gun was based on a series of patents granted to Fritz Walther in 1928–9. It was advertised as 170mm overall, 109mm high, 22mm thick, and chambered for the popular 7.65mm Auto or 9mm Short cartridges. The barrel measured 98mm, and the guns weighed about 600gm. A detachable box magazine was carried in the butt. The earliest catalogue illustrations show 'The New Walther Police Model' with a slide marked *Waffenfabrik Walther. Zella-Mehlis (Thür.)* over *Walther's Patent. Cal. 7.65m/m* ahead of the banner trademark, which lies in front of the safety-lever thumbpiece. No gun has yet been found matching this artist's impression. The Walther banner is shown moulded into the base of the injection-moulded plastic grips, a signal pin is present above the hammer, and a magazine extension could be supplied to order. No 'Mod. PP' mark appears on the gun; Walther apparently intended to call it 'Model 10', continuing the previous numerical sequence, but had a last-minute change of mind.

The Polizei-Pistole was a better weapon than the Little Tom; it was strong, durable in spite of its complexity, elegantly designed and cleverly packaged. It had no peer in 1930, and exerts as strong an influence on the design of personal-defence weapons today as it did 70 years ago.

The outstanding feature is the trigger/safety mechanism, which influenced so many rival designs. The basic unit consists of seven parts. Pressure on the trigger draws the trigger bar forward, rotating the hammer by the action of the sear bar on the hammer-lifting arm. Simultaneously, the sear lifts the hammer lock. Only when the hammer lock is fully elevated can the hammer strike the firing pin; the passage of hammer to pin is otherwise prevented by the addition of a hammer lock on the hammer-body projection. When the lifting arm has rotated the hammer to its rearward limit, the sear disengages and the hammer flies forward to a position where (as the hammer lock has been lifted) it can strike the head of the firing pin. The gun then fires. The slide retreats, forcing the hammer back until it can engage the sear. The trigger bar has been disconnected from the sear during the recoil stroke, and the firer must release the trigger before the trigger bar can be pulled back to re-engage the sear.

The trigger mechanism can also be operated by thumb-cocking the hammer, reducing the pressure required to release the hammer from the sear and improving accuracy.

The safety catch is applied by pressing the thumb-lever protruding from the left side of the slide above the grip to rotate the transverse stem of the catch. The solid portion of the catch spindle rotates through a hole cut in the firing-pin body, effectively preventing the pin from moving forward or back. Simultaneously, the hammer, which would normally strike the firing pin owing to the cut-away rear portion of the catch spindle, is prevented from moving right forward by the solid spindle surface. Further rotation of the thumb lever trips the hammer-disconnecting lever, allowing the hammer to fly forward towards the firing pin. But it actually strikes the hammer lock, and additional safety is provided by the catch spindle and the positive firing-pin lock. The inertia-type firing pin, now mechanically locked by the catch-spindle cutouts, can no longer move forward to strike the primer of a chambered cartridge, no matter now hard the gun may be dropped on the ground or thrown at a wall.

The dismantling system derives from that of the Model 9. The PP slide can be removed simply by clearing the gun, cocking the action, pulling down on the trigger-guard bow, and pulling the slide to the rear. The slide then disengages the frame and can be slid gently forward.

Offered to the commercial market in the middle of 1930, the Polizei-Pistole was an instant success. It was originally intended as a small holster pistol, but could easily be carried in a pocket. The Prussian state police soon asked for a smaller version, to be carried in a shoulder holster. The result was

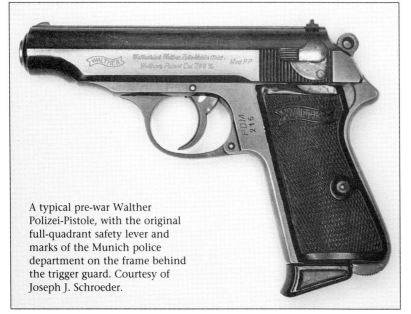

A typical pre-war Walther Polizei-Pistole, with the original full-quadrant safety lever and marks of the Munich police department on the frame behind the trigger guard. Courtesy of Joseph J. Schroeder.

The difference in the size of the Walther PP and
PPK is emphasised in these pictures of post-war
Interarms-marked (but Maurhin made) guns,
reproduced to a common scale.

'Polizei-Pistole, Kriminal' or 'PPK'. The origin of this particular designation, however, remains in question. Explanations offered for the 'K' suffix include *Kriminalpolizei* (plain-clothes police), *kurz* ('short') and *kleine* ('small'), even though these abbreviations could all have been written 'KPP'.

The first PPK seems to have reached the commercial market in 1931. The prototype had a reduced-size PP grip, with front and back straps; the perfected version had only a front strap and an enveloping one-piece grip.

Walther was more than satisfied with the 7.65mm Polizei-Pistole, and sales had been most gratifying. In 1933 6.35mm and 5.6mm lfb (.22 Long Rifle rimfire) versions appeared, obtainable to special order. However, fewer than 500 6.35mm pistols had been made when the option was abandoned in 1935. The *Cal. 6,35m/m.* slide marking was hand-stamped rather than mechanically rolled, and is notably uneven.

Polizei-Pistolen were widely favoured by police, paramilitary and military authorities alike. Some of the political formations of the Third Reich period began to buy them as early as 1935–6. In 1939, when serial numbers reached the million mark, each individual Walther pistol-type was separated into its own sequence. The PP and PPK were then numbered from 100001P and 100001K respectively. Production continued until the end of the Second World War, the highest known numbers being in the region of 397000P and 433500A for the PP and PPK respectively. The 'A' suffix replaced 'K' during the war.

Although Polizei-Pistolen were extremely successful, engineering changes were made even in the first phase of production. The earliest guns had a needlessly complicated split or two-piece firing pin, and a bent riband spring for the firing-pin lock. The mechanism had been changed by the introduction of the PPK in 1931. The earliest

PPK had a shortened grip with only a front strap to support enveloping or 'wrap-around' one-piece grips. However, as the sear rotated through an aperture cut in the frame-side, even the PP frame is weak in the area of the back-strap joint. Alloy frames were particularly prone to crack, and the machining process was soon changed to allow a bridge of metal to act as a strengthener. Enforced changes were made to the sear, and the separate trigger-bar actuating spring was discarded when Walther realised that the trigger spring could be bent far enough to fulfil both functions.

Additional changes to the safety catch were made in the mid-1930s, when the support block for the firing pin, previously retained by a pin, was machined integrally with the slide. The barrel was rebated for part of its length to increase the clearance for the recoil spring, and the hammer was grooved to clear the modified signal pin. The oldest frames can be identified by the large recess in the right side for the riband spring.

Many Polizei-Pistolen lacked the signal pin that protruded from the rear of the slide above the hammer to show when there was a cartridge in the chamber. This feature was originally optional, but proved so popular that it was standardised after 1933. As late as 1935, however, Polizei-Pistolen were being offered for 46.50 Reichsmarks with the signal pin or 45 Reichsmarks without it. The pins were omitted from pistols made during the last months of the Second World War to simplify production.

The 90° safety catch was replaced about 1938 by a short-throw or 60° pattern, necessitating changes in the slide. The original heavyweight hammer, with a small transverse hole, was replaced at about this time by a lightened pattern.

Apart from changes of slide marking-die, no important alterations were made until the noticeable step behind the rear

trigger-guard pivot, below the magazine catch, was eliminated in 1943 to save machine time.

Some pistols, particularly from pre-war production, were specially finished; some wore nickel plating, others were chromed, and a few were even etched or engraved for special presentation. Gold plating and inlaying, gilding and silver-finishing were also occasionally used, although the vast majority of pistols were quite standard. A few even had experimental grey phosphate finishes, comparable to Parkerisation.

The PP and PPK originally bore commercial crown-over-'N' ('crown/N') nitro-proof marks, until they were replaced from 1 April 1940 by an eagle/N mark. Police-issue weapons usually bear a large eagle-and-swastika mark, the highly stylised swastika taking the form of a circle.

Other identification marks include the encircled 'RZM' of the Reichszeugmeisterei, which accepted guns for the Schutzstaffel; D.R.P., usually on the grip straps, indicating service with the postal authorities, or Deutsches Reichsost; NSKK or N.S.K.K., rarely encountered, identifying the Nationalsozialistische Kraftfahrkorps, or state transport service; S.A. or, more rarely, S.A. der N.S.D.A.P. for the Sturm-Abteilung; R.F.V. for the Reichsforstverwaltung or state forestry service; R.J. for the Reichs-Justizministerium; and a series of Bavarian police marks, taking the form of P.D.N. for Polizei-Direktion Nürnberg. Guns marked Rplt. (*Rigspoliti*) were used in Denmark after the end of the Second World War.

POLIZEI-PISTOLE RIVALS

The instantaneous success of the double-action Polizei-Pistole in post-1930 Germany caused consternation among rival gunmakers. Almost overnight, the PP had made guns such as the Sauer Behörden-Modell and the older Mausers obsolescent. Though Sauer and Mauser both attempted to introduce modernised versions of their traditional guns (e.g., the Mauser Modell 1934), they could not hope to compete with the Walther.

The first real rival for the Walther PP was the Menz PB Special (for *Polizei und Behörde*, 'police and officials'), which appeared in 1937. Chambered for the 7.65mm Auto round, the PB Special was 155mm long and had a seven-round magazine. The safety catch slid vertically in a channel on the left side of the slide above the retraction grips.

However, despite some good features, the PB Special was not as sturdy as the Walther, nor was its promoter powerful enough to make real impact on the market. Identical guns were made for the Lignose group, which had purchased Menz some years earlier. Their slides were marked THEODOR BERGMANN ERBEN/WAFFENFABRIK SUHL/SPECIAL MODEL, instead of the otherwise customary AUGUST MENZ WAFFENFABRIK SUHL/PB "SPECIAL". Both patterns had injection-moulded plastic grips marked `Special'.

Mauser-Werke AG of Oberndorf am Neckar perfected the 'Hahn-Selbstspanner, Modell C' (HSc) after making a series of prototypes in the late 1930s. The new pistol, which was elegant and effective, did not appear on the commercial market until after the proof laws changed on 1 April 1940; no guns have been seen with anything other than 'eagle/N' proofs. Production commenced with a test or tooling series numbered from V1001 up to perhaps V1025, before work began in earnest at No. 700000, theoretically continuing the previous 7.65mm series, though there is no evidence that the last 50,000 pre-HSc numbers were ever used. The only evidence of dating is provided by the change from 'eagle/655' to 'eagle/135' army inspector's marks in 1942. Production of the HSc ended under French control in February 1946,

The single-action Mauser 'Model 34' pistol could not hope to compete with the Walther Polizei-Pistole, and was rapidly superseded.

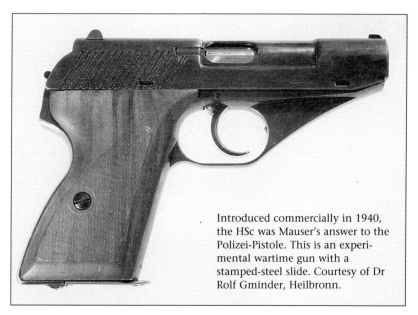

Introduced commercially in 1940, the HSc was Mauser's answer to the Polizei-Pistole. This is an experimental wartime gun with a stamped-steel slide. Courtesy of Dr Rolf Gminder, Heilbronn.

when serial numbers had exceeded 967000.

The only other manufacturer to produce a double-action personal defence pistol of PP type was J. P. Sauer & Sohn of Suhl. Offered in the normal 7.65mm Auto or 9mm Short chamberings, the Sauer Model 38-H was one of the most interesting designs in the personal-defence class. It was 160mm long, had an 85mm barrel and weighed about 620gm without its eight-round magazine. An

enclosed hammer was developed to overcome complaints made against the Walther and Mauser designs – that dirt would enter the mechanism through the hammer slot, or that the hammer spur could catch on the lining of a pocket. The Sauer 38-H was cocked not by thumbing back a spur-hammer but instead by operating a lever protruding on the left side of the frame from the front upper edge of the grip. The lever could also be used to de-cock the mecha-

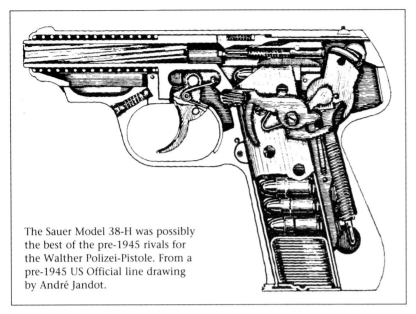

The Sauer Model 38-H was possibly the best of the pre-1945 rivals for the Walther Polizei-Pistole. From a pre-1945 US Official line drawing by André Jandot.

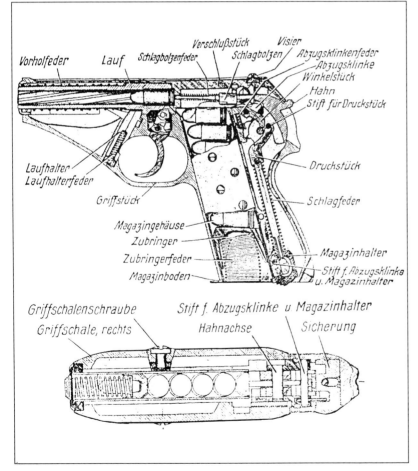

A longitudinal section of the Mauser HSc from Fischer's *Leitfaden für die Ordnungspolizei* (1943).

nism, which could then be fired (assuming the safety catch had been released) simply by pulling through on the trigger. The Sauer 38-H was made until 1945, though quality declined appreciably in the last months of hostilities.

Even though the German firearms industry collapsed in 1945, these double-action blowbacks continued to be influential. A surprising number of post-war designs has been based on them, while the Walther PP/PPK series and the Mauser HSc were eventually returned to production. The Walthers were initially licensed to Manufacture de Machines du Haut-Rhin ('Manurhin') of Mulhouse, and the HSc was briefly manufactured by Mauser-Jagdwaffen – the sporting-gun division of Mauser-Werke GmbH of Oberndorf – before the project was sold in the early 1980s to the Italian sporting-gun maker Armi Renato Gamba (now Società d'Armi Bresciane) of Gardone Val Trompia.

Ironically, only the Sauer 38-H failed to influence post-war designs directly. It is believed that a handful of prototypes were made in the company's new Eckenförde factory in the late 1950s, with the intention of marketing a 'Model 58', but the project came to nothing. The modern SIG-Sauer P230, however, is a lineal descendant of the 38-H.

THE MODERN AUTOMATIC PISTOL

It is very tempting to see the post-war development of the handgun simply as a continuation of the refinement begun before 1945. A grain of truth undoubtedly exists in this argument, but, judged as a whole, it is far too simplistic. The influence of the Browning GP-35 ('High Power') on military weapons or the Walther PP and its derivatives on personal-defence pistols remains surprisingly strong. Yet scope has always existed for enterprise and innovation in both fields; many agencies have been willing to try.

Typical post-1950 blow-back pistols. **Top left:** An Italian 6.35mm Beretta Model 950B, with a distinctive tipping barrel. **Top right:** The Italian .22 rimfire Bernardelli Model 68. **Centre left:** The Spanish-made .22 LR rimfire Astra Model 7000. **Centre right:** The American Davis Industries P-32. **Left:** the American Bauer .25, a copy of the pre-war FN-Browning Baby. Courtesy of the manufacturers.

The personal-defence market is still dominated by simple small-calibre blowbacks, many of them derived from the original 6.35mm Browning of 1905. The best of these tiny guns, however, now incorporate double-action triggers and similar refinements. The Walther TPH is a particularly good example of this trend, but many guns of broadly comparable form are being made in the USA.

Makers of Modern Pocket Automatic Pistols

NOTE: guns are chambered for 6.35mm Auto (.25 ACP) unless stated otherwise.

Accu-Tek, Inc., Chino, California
    AT-32 (7.65mm), AT-380 (9mm Short).
American Derringer Corporation, Waco, Texas, USA
    Derringer Auto.
American Firearms Mfg. Co. Inc., San Antonio, Texas, USA
    AFM Mark X.
Astra-Unceta y Compañía, Guernica, Spain
    Astra 2000 Cub (also in .22), Astra 7000 (.22).
Auto-Nine Corporation, Parma, Idaho, USA
    Auto Nine (.22).
Bauer Firearms Corporation, Fraser, Michigan, USA
    Bauer 25.
Pietro Beretta SpA, Gardone Val Trompia, Italy
    M2 (.22), M4 (.22), M20, M21A (also in .22), M34 Bantam, M418 Panther, M420, M421, M950, M950B, M950BS (also in .22), M951 Jetfire and Minx (.22).
Vincenzo Bernardelli & Co. SNC, Gardone Val Trompia, Italy
    M68 (also in .22), PA 'Baby' (.22).
Colt's Manufacturing Co. Inc., Hartford, Connecticut, USA
    Junior, Mustang 380 (9mm Short), Mustang Plus Two (9mm Short).
Davis Industries, Mira Loma, California, USA
    P-32 (7.65mm), P-380 (9mm Short).

Fraser Arms Company, Inc., Fraser, Michigan, USA
    Fraser 25.
FTL Marketing Corporation, USA
Industria Armi Galesi, Collobeato/Brescia, Italy
    Models 6, 9 and 506.
Grendel, Inc., Rockledge, Florida, USA
    P-10 (9mm Short).
Intratec Inc., Miami, Florida, USA
    Intratec 22 (.22), Intratec 25.
Iver Johnson's Arms Inc., Jacksonville, Arkansas, USA
    TP22B (.22), TP25B.
Jennings Firearms Inc., Stateline, Nevada, and Irvine, California, USA
    J-22 (.22), J-25.
Korriphila-Präzisionsmechanik GmbH, Ulm/Donau, Germany
    TP-70.
Llama–Gabilondo y Compañía, Elgoeibar, Spain
    Models 17 and 18.
Lorcin Engineering Co. Inc., Mira Loma, California, USA
    L-25.
MAB–Manufacture d'Armes de Bayonne, Bayonne, France
    Model B.
Michigan Armament, Inc., Detroit, Michigan, USA
    Guardian 27C or 270.
OMC, Inc., El Monte, California, USA
    Back Up 380 (9mm Short).
Phoenix Arms Company, Ontario, Canada
    HP-22 (.22), HP-25.
Pretoria Arms Factory, Pretoria, Republic of South Africa
    Junior, 'P.A.F.'
Raven Arms Inc., Industry, California, USA
    P-25.
Karl Arndt Reck, Lauf bei Nürnberg, Germany
    P-8, SM-11.
Rhöner Sportwaffenfabrik GmbH, Germany
    Model 115.
Rigarmi–Rino Galesi, Collobeato/Brescia, Italy
Sabatti & Tanfoglio, Gardone Val Trompia, Italy
    Sata.
L. W. Seecamp & Co. Inc., New Haven, Connecticut, USA
    LWS-32 (7.65mm).
Smith & Wesson Inc., Springfield,

Massachusetts, USA
    Escort M-61 (also in .22).
Star–Bonifacio Echeverria SA, Eibar, Spain
    CK Starlet, CO, CU Starlet.
Steel City Arms, Inc., Pittsburgh, Pennsylvania, USA
    Double Deuce (.22), Two Bit Special.
Sterling Arms Corporation, Lockport, New York State, USA
    Model 300, Model 302 (.22).
Sundance Industries, North Hollywood, California, USA
    A-23.
Armi Giuseppe Tanfoglio, Gardone Val Trompia, Italy
    GT-22 (.22), GT-25.
Forjas Taurus SA, Porto Alegre, Brazil
    PT-22 (.22), PT-25.
Unique–Manufacture d'Armes de Pyrénées Françaises, Hendaye, France
    Mikros (also in 7.65mm), Mikros Model K.
Carl Walther GmbH, Ulm/Donau, Germany
    TP, TPH (both also in .22).
Wilkinson Arms, Parma, Idaho, USA
    Diana (also in .22).
A. Zoli & Co. SNC, Gardone Val Trompia, Italy

The larger and more sophisticated personal-defence designs are typified by the Walther PP/PPK group and the Soviet Makarov. The post-war history of the Walther Polizei-Pistole is particularly interesting, as guns are still being made nearly seventy years after their introduction. Initially prevented by the Allies from making firearms, Walther reached agreement with Manufacture de Machines du Haut-Rhin ('Manurhin') of Mulhouse-Bourtzwiller in Alsace in the spring of 1954. French-made Polizei Pistolen reached the commercial market in the summer of 1955, the first batch being purchased in its entirety by the Thalson Import Company of San Francisco. Thalson continued to import the Manurhin- Walthers for only a short period, the agency subsequently passing to Interarms of Alexandria, Virginia.

Manurhin made the PP and PPK in 7.65 and 9mm Short (.32 and .380 ACP), together with rimfire derivatives of both basic designs and a series of special sport and sport-target guns. They were essentially similar mechanically to pre-1945 Walthers, although the design of the firing pin and the safety catch was simplified. Serial numbers began arbitrarily at 10001 for the PP and 100001 for the PPK; 7.65mm-calibre guns had plain numbers, whereas the 9mm Short (.380 ACP) variety had an 'A' suffix letter and .22 rimfires were suffixed 'LR'. Once numbers on the Polizei-Pistolen reached 100000 they recommenced at 300001.

Manurhin-made guns bore the company's distinctive cogwheel trademark on the left side of the slide, between MANUFACTURE DE MACHINES above DU HAUT-RHIN at the front of the slide and LIC.EXCL.WALTHER above 'Mod. PP Cal. 7,65mm' towards the rear. The top of most plastic grips bore the Manurhin trademark, but the base displayed 'Lic. Walther PP'. The words MADE IN FRANCE were added to the slides of guns intended for export to the USA and other countries where laws required the origin of goods to be clearly marked.

Guns were made in France under the Manurhin banner until 1961, but were thereafter shipped to Germany, assembled, given standard Ulm/Donau slide markings, and proved in Baden-Württemberg. The slides displayed the Walther banner ahead of *Carl Walther Waffenfabrik Ulm/Do* over

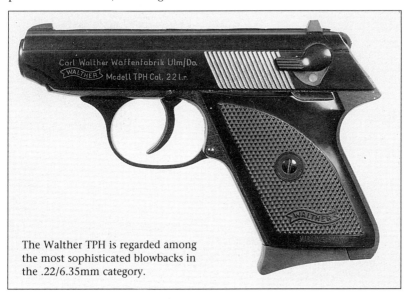

The Walther TPH is regarded among the most sophisticated blowbacks in the .22/6.35mm category.

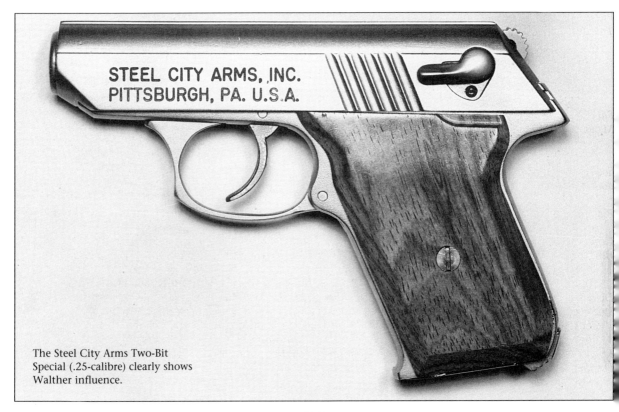

The Steel City Arms Two-Bit Special (.25-calibre) clearly shows Walther influence.

Modell PP Cal. 7.65mm. Finally, in 1964, the production machinery was shipped back to Germany.

The forcible removal of Walther from the roster of gunmakers in 1945 allowed rivals to copy the Polizei-Pistole with impunity. The resemblance to the PP is largely superficial in some guns, particularly from manufacturers whose expertise did not extend to double-action triggers and complex safety arrangements, but others – more enterprising or more certain of their production methods – copied the entire gun.

Makers of Modern Double-action Personal-defence Pistols

NOTE: guns chamber 7.65mm Auto cartridges unless otherwise stated.

American Arms Corporation, Jacksonville, Arkansas, USA
Eagle.
Astra–Unceta y Compañía, Guernica.
A-60 (also in 9mm Short), A-5000 Constable (also in .22 or 9mm Short).
Pietro Beretta SpA, Gardone Val Trompia, Italy
M70S (9mm Short), M81 and M81BB, M82BB, M84 and M84BB (9mm Short), M85BB (9mm Short), M86 (9mm Short), M87BB (.22).
Fábrica de Armas Bersa SA, Ramos Mejia, Argentina
Models 83 and 85 (both 9mm Short).
Società d'Armi Bresciane (SAB), Gardone Val Trompia, Italy
See 'Renato Gamba'.
Bulgarian state rifle factory
B-1300 (9mm Makarov).
Ceskoslovenská Zbrojovka, Brod and Uhersky Brod, Czechoslovakia
CZ 83 (also in 9mm Short), vz. 50, vz. 70.
Detonics, Inc., Seattle and Bellevue, Washington, USA
Pocket Nine (9mm Parabellum), Pocket 380 (9mm Short)
Erma-Werke GmbH & Co., München-Dachau, Germany
P-459 (9mm Short), P-552 (.22), RX-22 (.22).

Fabrique Nationale Herstal SA, Herstal, Belgium
140 DA (also in 9mm Short).
Femaru és Szerszámgépgyár NV, Budapest, Hungary
AP, APK, FP-9R, R-61, Walam.
Renato Gamba SpA, Gardone Val Trompia, Italy
RGP-80 and RGP-81 (also in 9mm Short and 9mm Police).
Rino Galesi, Collobeato/Brescia, Italy
Hijo Militar or Rigarmi (also in .22).
Heckler & Koch GmbH, Oberndorf/

Neckar, Germany
HK-4 (also in .22, 6.35mm and 9mm Short).
Indian Arms Corporation, Detroit, Michigan, USA
Indian 380 (9mm Short).
Interarms, Alexandria, Virginia, USA
PP, PPK, PPK/S.
Izhevsk ordnance factory, Izhevsk, USSR/Russia
PM (9mm Makarov), PSM (5.45mm).
Kirikkale Tüfek Fb, Ankara-Kurumu, Turkey

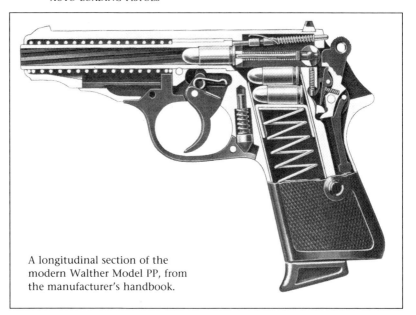

A longitudinal section of the modern Walther Model PP, from the manufacturer's handbook.

A typical post-1964 Walther Polizei Pistole, with German-language markings. Courtesy of Carl Walther GmbH, Ulm/Donau.

Kirikkale.

Zaklady Metalowe 'Lucznik', Radom, Poland

P-64 and P-83 (both 9mm Makarov).

Makina ve Kimya Endüstrisi, Ankara-Kurumu, Turkey

MKE.

Manufacture de Machines du Haut-Rhin, Mulhouse, France

PP, PPK (both also in 9mm Short).

Mauser-Jagdwaffen GmbH, Oberndorf/Neckar, Germany

HSc (also in 9mm Short).

J. P. Sauer & Sohn GmbH, Eckenförde/Holstein, Germany

See 'SIG'.

SIG–Schweizerische Industrie-Gesellschaft, Neuhausen/Rheinfalls, Switzerland

SIG-Sauer P230 (also in .22, 9mm Short or 9mm Police).

Sterling Arms Company, Lockport, New York State, USA

Sterling 440 Mk II (9mm Short).

Steyr-Daimler-Puch AG, Steyr, Austria

SP (also in 9mm Short?).

Carl Walther Sportwaffenfabrik GmbH, Ulm/Donau, Germany

PP, PPK, PPK/S (all also in 9mm Short); PP Super (9mm Short and 9mm Police).

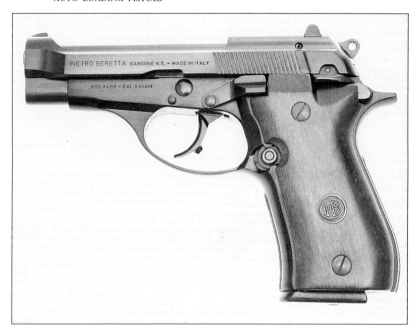

Among the earliest and most blatant copies were made by Kirikkale Tüfek Fb of Ankara-Kurumu from 1948 onwards for the Turkish army and, latterly, for commercial sale. The Kirikkale was a straightforward copy of the Polizei-Pistole in 7.65mm or 9mm Short, offering good quality despite occasional evidence of hand-finishing. The 7.65mm version had prominent recesses milled in the slide to save weight. Turkish army-issue guns were usually marked *T.C. Ordusu* above *Subaylarina Mahsus* ('Turkish army, for officers' use only'). Plagiarism even extended to a passable facsimile of the Walther banner-shape moulded into the lower portion of the original plastic grips, though the content read KIRIKKALE. When the moulding dies wore out, grips with a straight-sided banner became standard.

Kirikkale Tüfek was renamed Makina ve Kimya Endüstrisi in the late 1960s, the grip logo changing to an encircled 'MKE'. The MKE-marked guns were not normally dated, unlike many of their Kirikkale predecessors, which bore marks such as '1953' on the slide above the serial number. Turkish-made pistols had butt-heel magazine catches instead of the traditional Walther crossbolt through the frame behind the trigger. Slide markings included *Kirikkale Tüfek Fb. Cap. 9mm* on the earliest guns, then a transitional mark with an additional M.K.E. over the regular inscription, but the newest were simply marked with the encircled 'MKE' logo and

Included among double-action blow-back personal-defence pistols are – **Top left:** The Italian Beretta Model 84BB chambered for the 9mm Short cartridge. **Lower left:** The Argentine .380 Short Bersa Model 85. **Top right:** The Indian Arms Corporation 380. **Lower right:** The Heckler & Koch HK-4, which was remarkable for its interchangeable-barrel system.

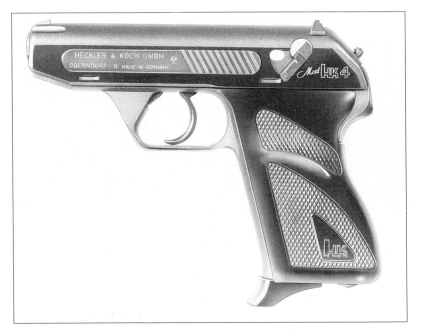

MADE IN TURKEY. The calibre mark often lay on the right side of the slide, accompanying the name of an American import agency. Among the most recent has been Firearms Center, Inc. ('FCI'), of Victoria, Texas.

The Hungarian state firearms factory in Budapest was another to begin production of Walther clones as soon as possible. The Walam 48 (known officially as the 'Pisztoly 48.M') was a near-copy of the Polizei-Pistole but exhibited some important differences. Apart from the superficial differences in the frame contours and the rounded overhang of the slide and frame at the rear, it had a vertically moving pin-type loaded-chamber indicator on top of the slide. There were twenty vertical retraction grooves and a modified safety-lever thumb-piece; a prominent hole was drilled through the trigger-guard bow web where it joined the frame, and a step was machined in the frame behind the trigger-guard pivot. The trigger guard was more angular than its Walther counterpart, and the hammer-head was solid rather than pierced. Magazines usually had distinctive plastic extensions to improve the handgrip.

The Walam usually had the Hungarian state emblem moulded into the grips. Slides were generally marked FEMARU ES SZER-SZAMGEPGYAR N.V. BUDAPEST over 48.M. KAL. 7.65mm. Other marks and a selection of differing grips have been identified, especially as these Hungarian pistols were exported in large numbers. Egypt, in particular, was an enthusiastic buyer in the late 1950s.

The AP and APK, sometimes sold commercially as the 'Attila', are closer copies of the PP and PPK respectively than the Walam. They were probably intended for the commercial market, whereas the Walam was conceived primarily as a military/police weapon. The R-61 was a modification of the 48.M, which it seems to have replaced in Hungarian military and police service. It is smaller than the 48.M, but chambers the 9mm Makarov cartridge instead of 9mm Short. The AP series lacked the loaded-chamber indicator, and the overhang of the slide and frame behind the grip was noticeably sharpened. The blued steel slides usually had only fifteen retraction grooves, the frames were invariably duraluminium, and the chequered thumbrest-type plastic grips (sometimes wood) rarely bore markings.

Large quantities of the AP66 were sold in Germany by Hege-Waffen GmbH of Schwäbisch Hall; their slides were inexplicably marked with a large cursive 'GSM' trademark ahead of MAUSER OBERAUDORF GERMANY above SLP1. Cal. 7.65mm (.32 Browning).

Small numbers of Polizei-Pistolen made in the German Democratic Republic after the end of the Second World War were probably assembled from parts found in the Zella-Mehlis factory in 1945. It is unlikely that the pistols were newly made, owing to the seizure of the original production machinery by the Russians. However, though the machining of the frames behind the trigger-guard pivot is very plain (characteristic of late-war production), most slides exhibit a perceptible change in contours at the muzzle. It is suspected that these were made to complete original parts sets. The distinctive GDR crown/'N' nitro proofmark appeared on the left side of the slide, the barrel and the frame. Serial numbers lay on the right side of the slide and frame, while the product-code 1001-0-Cal. 7,65 was struck into the left of the slide. Volkspolizei marks were also sometimes present, as these guns do not seem to have been issued to the state army. The injection-moulded chequered plastic grips were devoid of insignia.

Careful, if somewhat crude, copies of the PPK have also been made in the People's Republic of China. Minor changes were made in the trigger pull, but the most obvious identification features were the proliferation of unpolished machining marks, the crude copy of the standard Walther slide legend, and the appearance on the frame of 'Type 1' in ideographs. Surprisingly, the guns had injection moulded plastic grips, complete with the banner trademark, and a crossbolt-type magazine release. A lanyard loop lay on the butt heel, and 22 retraction grooves were milled vertically into the slide.

OTHER DOUBLE-ACTION DESIGNS

The origins of the Russian Makarov pistol lay in a handgun competition announced in 1945. Calibre was to either 7.62mm or 9mm, but submissions were to be smaller, lighter, more accurate, and more reliable than the existing recoil-operated Tokarev. Sever-

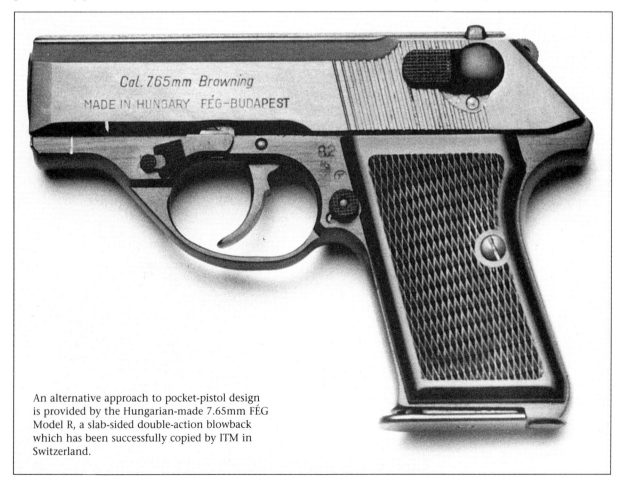

An alternative approach to pocket-pistol design is provided by the Hungarian-made 7.65mm FÉG Model R, a slab-sided double-action blowback which has been successfully copied by ITM in Switzerland.

al well-known Soviet designers prepared weapons, including Fedor Tokarev and Sergey Simonov, but testing revealed that the 9mm Makarov pistol was preferable. It was adopted by the Soviet Army in 1951 as the 'Pistolet Makarov' ('PM'). The gun was shorter and lighter than its predecessor and had a double-action trigger system.

However much the authorities protest that the blowback PM is entirely Soviet or Russian in character, it is hard to believe that inspiration had not been drawn from the Walther Polizei-Pistole – particularly as the Russians had taken possession of Walther's factory in Zella-Mehlis after the end of the Second World War.

Makarov copies have been made in several countries, including the German Democratic Republic and the People's Republic of China. The pistols are becoming increasingly common now that weapons are being smuggled in large numbers out of the former Communist bloc.

Another gun currently finding great favour in the West is the Czech CZ 83, which offers good manufacturing quality, a large magazine and a double-action trigger at the expense of considerable complexity.

The Beretta 80 series, which contains a wide range of guns in .22, 7.65mm and 9mm, has also achieved widespread distribution. These guns are characterised by double-action triggers, high-capacity magazines, an assortment of safety devices and a particularly elegant outline. The FN 140-DA and BDA-380, marketed by Fabrique Nationale of Herstal and the Browning Arms Company of Utah respectively, are both minor variants of the basic Beretta pattern.

EXPLORING THE LIMITS OF BLOWBACK

The 9mm Soviet pistol cartridge, or 9 x 18mm, is among the most powerful to be regularly chambered in blowback pistols. It has enjoyed a period in vogue in the West owing to the development by Hirtenberg in 1968–70 of the so-called 9mm Police round, which is really a Makarov made to different tolerances.

Walther began development in 1972 of a suitable 9mm Police pistol, the prototype PP Super being based on the standard Polizei-Pistole with a web running forward from the trigger guard. The slide and breechblock were strengthened, and a synthetic buffer softened the effects of recoil to reduce

The Colt .380 Mustang Pocketlite is a diminutive of the full-size locked breech Colt-Brownings. It is popular for its combination of power and compact dimensions. Courtesy of the Colt Firearms Manufacturing Company, Hartford, Connecticut.

The Walther P1K (with Manurhin markings) is a shortened version of a service weapon. Generally, guns of this type are less successful than the purpose-built blowbacks. Courtesy of Carl Walther GmbH, Ulm/Donau.

stress in the action. The safety system was redesigned to incorporate a positive hammer block, preventing the hammer striking the firing pin in all but the last stages of a deliberate trigger pull. The PP Super could not be fired even when dropped with the hammer down on a loaded chamber, because the hammer was held away from the firing pin by the positive lock. The pin itself was also immobilised.

The prototype pistols were gradually improved. The under-frame rib was deleted and the trigger guard was squared. The magazine catch was moved to the left side of the frame halfway down the trigger aperture to improve reloading time, while the angle between the grip and the bore was adjusted to improve snap-shooting performance.

Representatives of the German police authorities took some pre-production PP Super pistols to a shooting symposium at the Centre Nationale de Pérfectionnement de Tir in Paris in 1974, where a little over 2,000 rounds were fired in three series. Eight misfires were recorded, but all but three fired on a second pull of the double-action trigger. This is typical of the performance expected from a pistol of this type under normal conditions.

The PP Super was 170mm overall, with a 91mm barrel, and weighed 755gm unladen – not much greater than a standard Polizei-Pistole. It

was accepted for extended trials with the German police in 1974, and offered commercially a year later. However, the police preferred locked-breech designs and enthusiasm elsewhere has also been comparatively limited.

The trend towards super-power blowbacks has made no real headway, as the popular 9mm Short cartridge has proved notably difficult to dislodge from its position as market leader.

The Soviet Union pioneered an alternative approach in the 1970s with a unique service pistol in the unusually small calibre of 5.45mm. Developed by Tikhon Lashnev, Anatoliy Simarin and Lev Kulikov, the PSM ('Miniature semi-automatic pistol') was introduced in 1979. A blowback with a double-action hammer-type trigger mechanism, it has a surprisingly flat frame and a safety catch on the slide. The safety catch prevents the hammer reaching the firing pin while simultaneously locking the slide and the trigger in the forward position. When the catch is released, the hammer safety prevents the gun firing if it is accidentally dropped. A magazine safety ensures that the slide cannot be detached unless the chamber has been cleared and the loaded magazine has been removed. Distinctively flat light-alloy grips are latched to the frame, allowing the pistols to be dismantled without tools.

Anatoliy Simarin subsequently claimed that 'the main difficulty in designing the PSM lay in creating an extra-light and thin model (like a matchbox) without protrusions on its sides. This had to be combined with good combat characteristics and reliability, especially in difficult conditions.' The 5.45 x 18mm cartridge weighs merely 4.8gm, including a bullet of 2.4–2.6gm.

COMPACT LOCKED-BREECH DESIGNS

Another approach, particularly evident in recent years, has been to adapt conventional military-style handguns for dual-purpose roles which include concealment. Though many of these weapons have retained well-proven operating systems, such as variations of the Colt-Browning dropping-link or cam finger actuator, more radical approaches have sometimes been taken.

These included the Heckler & Koch Polizei-Selbstladepistole (PSP), which was submitted to the German police trials of the early 1970s. The story of these trials is well known; the results were inconclusive, and a range of suitable weapons was approved. The German state police forces were allowed to choose from the list, taking the P5 (Walther), P6 (SIG-Sauer P226) and P7 (Heckler & Koch PSP) in quantity. The PSP was a particularly interesting gun, as it embodied a blowback action delayed by a gas bleed and a squeeze-grip safety system which made a traditional manual lever superfluous.

It has now become fashionable for handgun manufacturers to provide 'compact' versions of their regular military designs. These are customarily short-butt/short-frame patterns, trading additional compactness for a reduction in cartridge capacity and a perceptible loss of muzzle velocity. Many observers believe that these guns – which are inevitably compromises – are not as

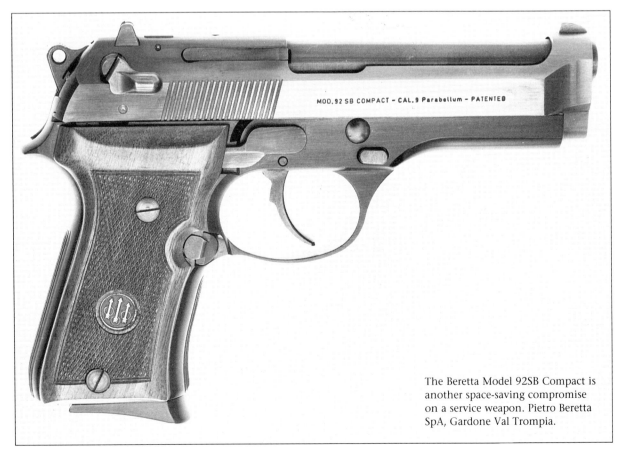

The Beretta Model 92SB Compact is another space-saving compromise on a service weapon. Pietro Beretta SpA, Gardone Val Trompia.

The ever-expanding range of Glock pistols includes this 9mm Parabellum Model 19 Compact. Courtesy of Glock GmbH, Deutsch-Wagram.

The Grendel P-10 typifies modern auto-loading pistols relying greatly on synthetic parts. This particular example has a prominent muzzle brake. Courtesy of Grendel, Inc.

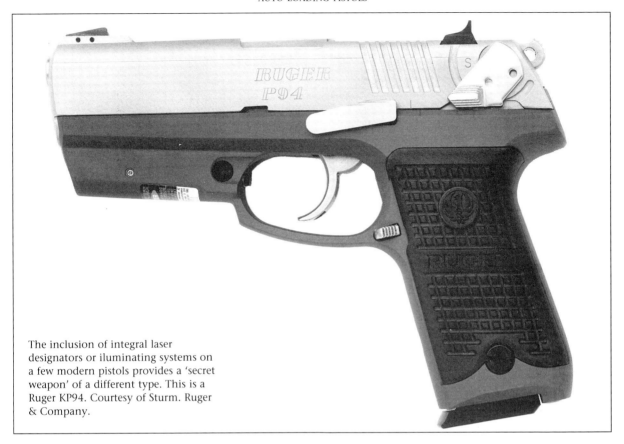

The inclusion of integral laser designators or iluminating systems on a few modern pistols provides a 'secret weapon' of a different type. This is a Ruger KP94. Courtesy of Sturm. Ruger & Company.

useful as the compact high-capacity 9mm double-action blowbacks, but the views are controversial.

THE UNDETECTABLE GUN?

Continual improvements in manufacturing technology have had important repercussions throughout the arms industry. Principal among these has been the development of synthetic components, once seen merely as replacements for minor parts such as triggers, release catches and magazines. The successful introduction of larger items, including entire frames, rapidly moved handgun design away from its traditional focus.

The advent of guns made largely of synthetic material has fuelled fears that armed terrorists will be able to evade X-ray surveillance. The principal target of unfounded suspicion has usually been the Austrian Glock, which will be seen as the true successor of the Browning GP-35 when the authoritative firearms history of the twentieth century is finally written.

The Glock is a variation of the well-proven Browning dropping-link breech mechanism, allied with a trigger-safety system based on a small blade set within the body of the trigger itself. The firer presses the blade before he can reach the trigger, almost without noticing, and in so doing disengages the safety mechanism.

Even the original Glock P-17 was a comparatively compact design, measuring only 188mm overall, but an ultra-compact version has also been made. However, these weapons retain metal barrels, a metal slide, metal springs and metal cartridges. There is no way in which they can elude a metal-detector or an X-ray system.

Can an undetectable weapon of this type be created within the confines of today's technology? No conventionally designed handgun chambering regular ammunition could currently be made in this form. However, the situation becomes less clear if design parameters are changed. An industry capable of making undetectable landmines could undoubtedly design synthetic weapons firing flechettes (elongated darts) from plastic-case cartridges. How close the arms industry has come to making weapons of this type is not clear, but reality is probably closer than anyone knows ... except those most closely involved.

HANDGUNS AND THE SILENCER

If there is one particular weapon associated with secrecy, it is the silencer-fitted pistol. This is undoubtedly due to its association with detective novels, gangster films and countless assassinations. For once, fact is not so very different from the legend.

THE EARLIEST DESIGNS

The silencer is a twentieth-century invention. The earliest patent was granted to Hiram Stevens Maxim in 1908, but it was left to his son, Hiram Percy Maxim, to take the first steps towards perfection. H. P. Maxim's first design, patented in

1908 two days after his father's, was similarly unsuccessful. It was not until March 1909, and the granting of US Patent 916,885, that he produced a practicable design. The tubular body of the 1909-type silencer contained baffles allowing propellant gas to expand within

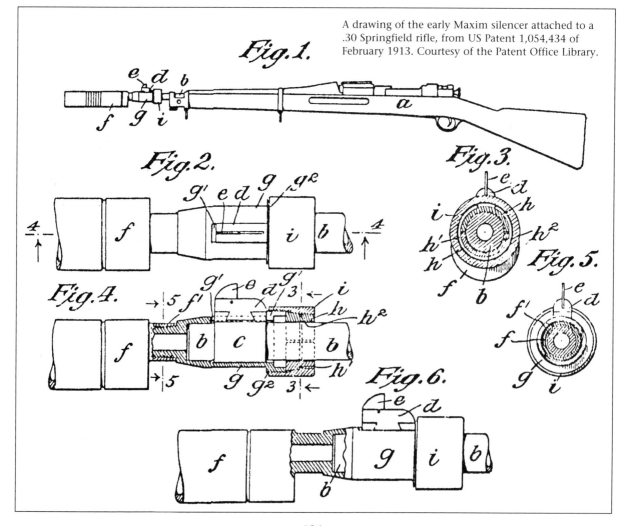

A drawing of the early Maxim silencer attached to a .30 Springfield rifle, from US Patent 1,054,434 of February 1913. Courtesy of the Patent Office Library.

the silencer body to lose much of its kinetic energy. When gas was ultimately vented to the atmosphere, therefore, it did so with much less noise than a normal discharge.

An improved form of this particular silencer was patented in the USA in May 1910. Although several different forms of the baffles were shown in the patent drawings, the version exploited commercially simply divided the silencer body into a series of compartments connected only by the small axial passage through which the bullet passed. The passage was usually offset towards the top of the baffles, so that the bulk of the large-diameter silencer body lay below the barrel axis. This allowed the open sights to be used.

These early silencers could not be dismantled for cleaning, and had to be thrown away if they clogged with propellant fouling. However, the Maxim Silent Firearms Company of New York sold large numbers of them commercially for a mere $3.50 apiece. Most were ultimately destined for

rifles, but there is evidence that some were adapted to handguns.

Maxim introduced an improved silencer for high-power military riflesin 1912, but tests in Britain and the USA were uninspiring. A competing design patented by Robert Moore, promoted by the Moore Silencer Company of Chicago, was more successful; 100 were acquired by the US Army in 1914.

The Hopkins & Allen Noiseless – a popular fitting on shooting-gallery rifles – was another successful American design, until the National Firearms Act passed in the USA in 1934 banned silencers completely. Similar legislation prevented them being used in Britain and France, although specific types of sound-moderator were permitted.

SILENCED HANDGUNS

To function effectively, silencers must be able to overcome two major problems when used with rifle ammunition: the expansion of gases at the muzzle until velocity is about twice the speed of sound, and the shock-wave created as the supersonic bullet cuts through the

atmosphere. Early attempts to silence full-power rifles proved to be abortive, and thoughts turned instead to providing special ammunition which was marginally subsonic. By removing the supersonic shock wave, this reduced problems to merely preventing the expanding gases from escaping until sufficient energy had been dissipated.

The problems scarcely affected handguns, as only a few cartridges are truly supersonic, e.g. the 7.62mm Tokarev, 7.65mm Parabellum or 7.63mm Mauser. Most silenced handguns, therefore, fire comparatively slow-moving projectiles. Among the most popular have been the 6.35mm and 7.65mm Auto rounds, 9mm Parabellum (transonic in some loadings) and the hard-hitting .45 ACP. None of these normally needs to be downgraded to function effectively in conjunction with silencers, though the 6.35mm and 7.65mm Auto are only marginally powerful enough to be effective man-stoppers.

Though fiction often tries to persuade otherwise, silencers can-

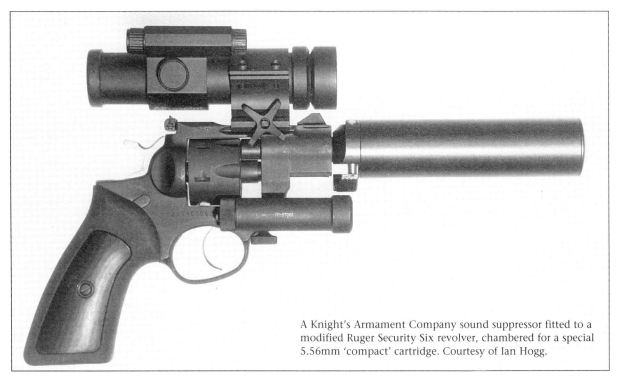

A Knight's Armament Company sound suppressor fitted to a modified Ruger Security Six revolver, chambered for a special 5.56mm 'compact' cartridge. Courtesy of Ian Hogg.

not be used in conjunction with standard revolvers, as the leakage of gas between the face of the cylinder and the rear of the barrel is too great. The one plausible exception to this rule would be a gas-seal design of the type pioneered in Belgium by Nagant, Pieper and others. The OGPU (the Russian secret police, predecessor of the KGB) allegedly adapted some 1895-pattern Nagant revolvers for Maxim-type silencers in the 1920s, but this has never been confirmed. The performance of the combination, if indeed it was ever tried, is unknown.

Originally patented in Belgium in 1894, these seven-shot revolvers fired a special 7.62mm cartridge with the bullet buried in an elongated neck. A fraction of a second before the hammer fell, a special lever in the trigger mechanism pressed the cylinder forward until the mouth of the chamber rode over the end of the barrel. This allowed cartridge-case neck to expand momentarily to seal the barrel/cylinder joint, reducing gas leaks to practically nothing. The consensus is that the complication was not worth the undeniable gain in performance, which was very modest. Yet 1895-type service revolvers were manufactured in quantity in the USSR until the summer of 1942. Among them were short-barrel, short-butt guns intended for concealment.

Several specialist manufacturers have recently returned to the gas-seal concept, fitting sound suppressors to a variety of revolvers. Knight's Armament Company of Vero Beach, Florida, for example, has offered a modification of the Ruger GP-100 chambering a special 5.56mm 'telescoped' subsonic cartridge. The baffle-type suppressor was similar to the snap-on type made by Knight for the Beretta M9. The overall length of the revolver/suppressor combination was about 13in, the weight totalling 3½lb. The manufacturer claimed that the normal noise level, 163 dB, dropped to 121 dB

when the suppressor was used. Though far from silent, this is sufficient to prevent the firing position being located.

With the exception of gas-seal revolvers, silenced handguns are either single-shot or semi-automatic pistols. The autoloaders have been much more popular, as they can be taken from production lines in quantity. Adaption is usually straightforward, particularly if the barrels already protrude from the slide. Unfortunately, the considerable weight of the silencer adversely affects the moving-barrel auto-loaders such as the Luger or the big Colt-Brownings. Changes sometimes have to be made in the return springs to handle the additional moving mass if auto-loading is to be maintained. The most popular silencer-fitted pistols, therefore, are fixed-barrel blowbacks with slides which reciprocate independently.

THE SECOND WORLD WAR
Although no silencer-fitted pistols were used during the First World War, the situation was very different in 1939. Research had undoubtedly been undertaken by the authorities in Germany and Russia, where the Gestapo and the OGPU/KGB had both experimented with assassination weapons. The Germans produced experimental auto-loading pistols and bolt-action carbines with integral silencers.

The general view was much more favourable to covert operations than it had been twenty years earlier. When the SOE and OSS were formed in Britain and the USA respectively, development of clandestine weapons began in earnest. Research produced crossbows, pneumatic dart guns, and a range of disguised explosives as well as silenced weapons. The most popular handguns were similar-looking .22 rimfire auto-loaders – the Woodsman, made in Hartford, Connecticut, by Colt's Patent Fire Arms Manufacturing Company, and a version of the pre-war Model

HD (the US-HD), made in nearby Hamden by the High Standard Manufacturing Company.

The Woodsman was fitted with a Maxim-type silencer, with the bore offset to allow the existing open sights to be used. The High Standard pistol, however, had a purpose-built silencer with the front sight on top of the silencer body. The barrel was reduced to the smallest permissible diameter and pierced by four rows of eleven circular vents. These allowed propellant gas to dissipate into a wire-mesh silencer insert, absorbing the energy of the propellant gas.

The High Standard silencer was surprisingly effective. Even though the life of the insert was very short, the gun could fire .22 Long Rifle cartridges with nothing more than a click. And even this could not be heard more than a few feet away.

The British SOE issued a few silenced .22 Webley & Scott single-shot target pistols for use when particularly accurate shooting was required. These avoided the mechanical noise which afflicted auto-loaders, even though they obviously could not fire a rapid back-up shot.

The Webley was replaced by the Welrod, developed by the Welwyn Experimental Laboratories in 1942. The single-shot 7.65mm Welrod Mark I, the first to be introduced, was little more than a tube with a detachable hand grip containing the seven-round magazine. The Welrod bolt was locked by turning the knob at the rear of the action, and a short grip safety protruded behind the magazine housing to guard against accidental discharge. Rudimentary open sights were provided. The Welrod barrel was comparatively short, ending mid-way along the tubular barrel shroud. Immediately ahead of the muzzle lay a self-sealing rubber baffle and a steel plate, then a short multi-ported tube or barrel extension to let propellant gases expand into the silencer body, and then another rubber baffle/steel plate assembly. When the gun was fired, the rubber baffles closed behind the projectile as it passed. Welrods could be carried in a special holster, made by jewellers Mappin & Webb, but could also be separated into two parts and carried suspended in special carrying loops sewn inside agents' trousers.

The 7.65mm Welrod was almost totally silent. However, it was regarded as ineffective and was rapidly replaced by the 9mm Welrod Mark I. This chambered 9mm Parabellum ammunition, reducing magazine capacity to six, but these rounds were too powerful for the silencer and the gun released gas with a perceptible hiss after it had been fired. The 9mm Mark IIA pistol was essentially similar to the bolt-action 9mm Mark I, but exhibited detail differences. It was to be made by BSA Guns Ltd.

A few Welrod-type pistols were made in the US Navy Gun Factory in 1944. Designated 'Hand Firing Device Mark 1', these .45-calibre weapons used the standard seven-round M1911A1 magazine.

The Wel-Wand was a single-shot .22-calibre weapon with an integral silencer. It was designed to be carried inside an agent's sleeve, along the forearm, but was suspended on an elastic strap from the type of harness associated with a shoulder holster. The Wel-Wand was to be pulled down into the hand, pressed hard against the intended victim (firing the gun with a muzzle-rod) and released to spring back instantly out of sight.

In addition to the Woodsman, HDM and Welrods, the agents of the SOE and OSS used pistols from a pool of non-regulation equipment. These were often selected according to the theatre of operations; an agent dropped into central Europe, for example, could select a silencer-fitted Czech vz. 37 service pistol (a small blowback), whereas a colleague serving in Italy would use a 1934-type Beretta. Among the guns known to have been used were PP and PPK-type Walthers, 1910-type Mausers, Webley & Scott .25 and .32 automatics, and even a Luger or two.

THE MODERN ERA

The lure of the silencer has endured to the present day, particularly in countries committed to the training of Special Forces or areas where political assassination is commonplace. However governments might attempt to underplay the existence of their own intelligence services, it is difficult to deny the existence of these weapons when they fall into opponents' hands. When US Air Force pilot Gary Powers was shot down over the Soviet Union on a clandestine reconnaissance mission in May 1960, triggering a worldwide political crisis, a silenced High Standard .22 US-HD pistol and several 50-round ammunition cartons

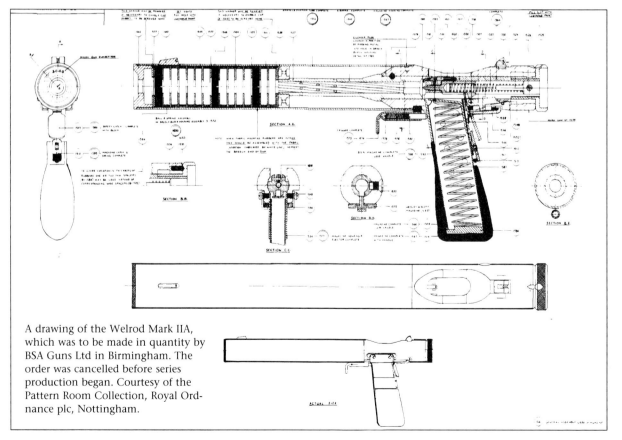

A drawing of the Welrod Mark IIA, which was to be made in quantity by BSA Guns Ltd in Birmingham. The order was cancelled before series production began. Courtesy of the Pattern Room Collection, Royal Ordnance plc, Nottingham.

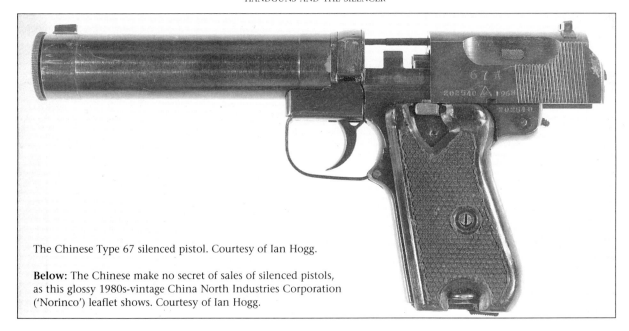

The Chinese Type 67 silenced pistol. Courtesy of Ian Hogg.

Below: The Chinese make no secret of sales of silenced pistols, as this glossy 1980s-vintage China North Industries Corporation ('Norinco') leaflet shows. Courtesy of Ian Hogg.

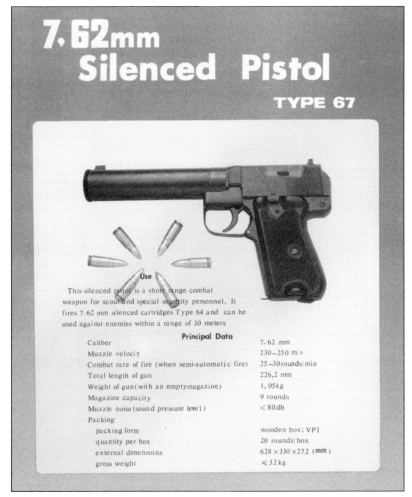

7.62mm
Silenced Pistol
TYPE 67

Use

This silenced pistol is a short range combat weapon for scout and special security personnel. It fires 7.62 mm silenced cartridges Type 64 and can be used against enemies within a range of 30 meters.

Principal Data

Caliber	7.62 mm
Muzzle velociy	230–250 m/s
Combat rate of fire (when semi-automatic fire)	25–30 rounds/min
Total length of gun	226,2 mm
Weight of gun (with an empty magazine)	1.05kg
Magazine capacity	9 rounds
Muzzle noise (sound pressure level)	<80db
Packing:	
packing form	wooden box; VPI
quantity per box	20 rounds/box
external dimensoins	628×330×272 (mm)
gross weight	<32kg

were retrieved from the wreck of his Lockheed U-2 spy-plane.

Handgun silencers are almost always bulky, but attempts have been made (particularly in the People's Republic of China) to integrate the silencer with special purpose-built pistols. The Chinese Type 64 could operate either as a conventional semi-automatic or as a single-shot pistol, as the slide could be locked shut to reduce the amount of mechanical noise generated in the normal auto-loading action. The gun fired a special 7.65 x 17mm cartridge similar to the 7.65mm Auto, and was locked by a rotating bolt cammed into engagement with the breech as the slide closed. In single-shot mode, the bolt head remained locked until a latch on the top of the slide was pressed. A cam inside the slide engaged a projection on the bolt head to unlock the breech once the slide had been retracted about 8mm. The large-diameter barrel casing contained two sound-suppressing chambers and a perforated baffle-type silencer filled with mesh. When the gun fired, propellant gas leaked into the silencer body through twelve small barrel ports, circulated around the baffles to lose energy, then re-entered the

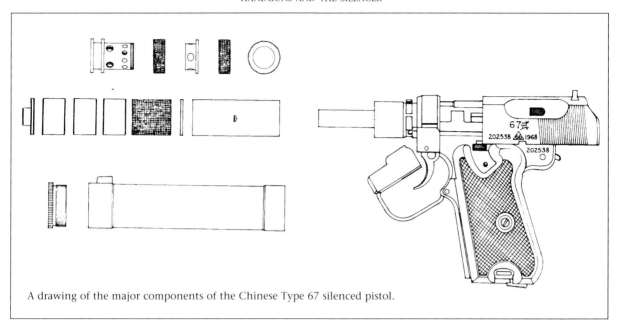

A drawing of the major components of the Chinese Type 67 silenced pistol.

bore to emerge from the muzzle at such low velocity that virtually nothing was audible.

The Type 67 was essentially similar to the Type 64, but was fitted with an improved tubular silencer. North Korea has also produced a silenced handgun in small numbers, but this was simply based on the Type 64 service pistol, little more than the venerable 1900-model FN-Browning blow-back, and could only fire semi-automatically.

The performance of these guns has been the subject of controversy, some firers being impressed with the lack of noise while others were dissatisfied with the lack of power. The unique 7.65mm cartridge limited effective range to 40-50m.

Like many other silenced pistols, these Chinese products are inevitably compromises. However, enough were captured in Vietnam in the 1960s to persuade the US Navy to begin development of a silenced Smith & Wesson 9mm automatic pistol for SEAL teams. The gun was apparently intended to silence watchdogs; it was nicknamed 'Hush Puppy', a term which had been introduced by the OSS during the Second World War to

denote a pneumatic dart gun and a special type of tranquillised dog food. Initially designated WOX-13A, the new Smith & Wesson was developed around the Model 39 (first prototypes) and Model 59 (later examples). The pistols were modified in minor respects, as the barrel was lengthened to protrude from the slide and the return springs were altered to handle the extra weight of the silencer attachment.

The principal claims to novelty lay in the design of the waterproof silencer, protection being sought by Richard D. Plenge of Silver Springs, Maryland, in August 1969. The relevant patent was granted in July 1972 and assigned to the 'United States of America as represented by the Secretary of the Navy'. The silencer consisted of a tube inside an annular chamber, with O-ring seals between the silencer body and the barrel-muzzle, as well as between the end-caps and body of the silencer itself. The silencing unit comprised alternating polyurethane plugs, disc washers and spacer rings, each plug having a central cross-cut to allow the bullet to pass. Special rubber plugs were supplied to fit over the apertures in the ends of the silencer,

over the muzzle of the gun (if the silencer had been detached), and even into the chamber to prevent water entering the bore from the rear. The bullet-shaped chamber-plug had an O-ring seal of its own, but had to be ejected manually before the gun could be used. The muzzle-plugs, however, were designed to be shot out if necessary.

After initial problems had been overcome, the WOX-13A was approved for special service as the 'Pistol, Mark 3 Model 0'. It was about 12.75in long and weighed 38oz without the magazine. Special green-tip 9mm Mark 144 Model 0 cartridges were issued, relying on 158-grain bullets to reduce muzzle velocity to subsonic levels. However, the life of the silencer insert was only 30 shots. The accessory kit issued with each Mark 3 Model 0 pistol contained 24 special cartridges and a replacement silencer insert.

Although some companies still prefer purpose-built equipment – Law Enforcement International Ltd, for example, built the LEI Mark 2 Silenced Pistol on the basis of the .22 Ruger auto-loader – the current favourite is a clip-on suppressor such as the Knight design

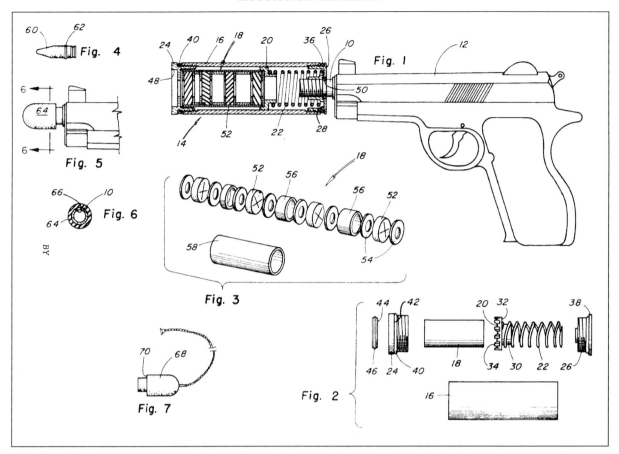

Above: The US Navy 'Hush Puppy' silencer, from US Patent 3,677,132 granted in July 1972. Courtesy of the Patent Office Library.

for the US 9mm Beretta M9. Accessories of this type can usually be fitted to standard-issue guns without modification, and are seen as part of a system or 'package' by major manufacturers such as Heckler & Koch.

SOVIET DESIGNS

Very few purpose-built silenced pistols have been built in the West in recent years, reliance being placed on minor modifications of standard designs. Only the Soviet Union, intent on perpetuating the Cold War, has continued development on a large scale. The APB was adapted from the 9mm Stechkin (APS), which had failed in its role as pistol/submachine-gun. The

detachable silencer, 230mm long with an external diameter of 35mm, was basically a 1.5mm-broad annular chamber around the barrel, into which propellant gas bled from the barrel ports. Four radial holes lay about 15mm from the front of the chamber, and eight more appeared about 15mm from the muzzle. Once the bullet had emerged from the muzzle, the gas remaining in the silencer – which had lost a substantial amount of its energy – re-entered the bore and was exhausted at the muzzle. The frame of the pistol was extended to support the rear of the silencer body, and a separate steel-rod butt could be attached when required. Clips on the butt held the silencer when it was detached from the gun.

The PB, a silenced version of the PM (Makarov), was designed by a group working in the Tula ordnance factory. The slide was com-

bined with a 32mm-diameter shroud filled with six layers of fine steel mesh, and the barrel was lengthened to 105mm. Propellant gas could bleed through ports cut radially in the barrel, through the mesh, back into the barrel and then out through the multi-baffle silencer held to the front of the shroud by a small spring-catch ahead of the frame. Although the PB incorporated many characteristics of the standard Makarov, changes were made to the heavier-than-normal slide to accommodate the silencer. The return spring was moved from its customary position around the barrel to the rear of the grip behind the magazine well. The PB was 195mm long

Right: Afghani Mujahedin examine a Tokarev pistol, probably a Chinese-made example, fitted with a Maxim-type silencer.

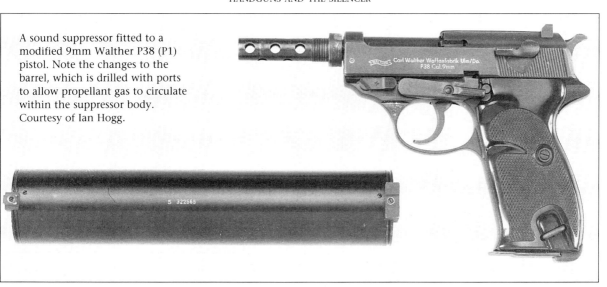

A sound suppressor fitted to a modified 9mm Walther P38 (P1) pistol. Note the changes to the barrel, which is drilled with ports to allow propellant gas to circulate within the suppressor body. Courtesy of Ian Hogg.

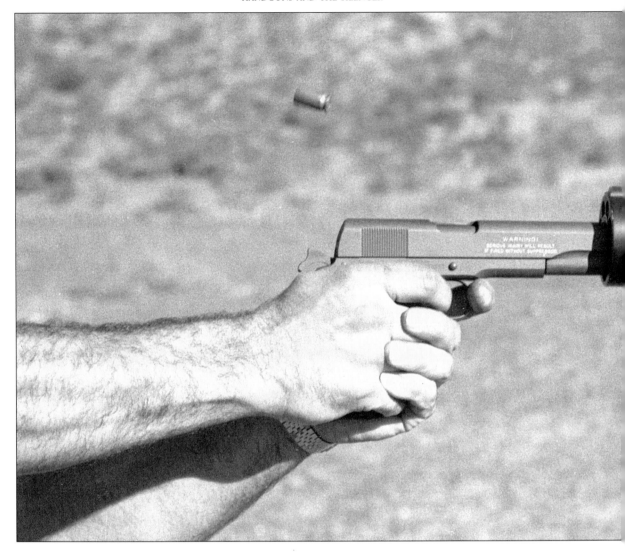

(310mm with the auxiliary silencer chamber attached) and weighed 950gm empty. Muzzle velocity of standard 9mm ball ammunition dropped from about 340m/sec to 290m/sec.

The MSP-2 and PSS represent an alternative approach to silencing, relying on special SP-3 (MSP-2) and SP-4 (PSS) cartridges instead of bulky accessories. The goal was to reduce size to a minimum, making the special pistols difficult to recognise at a glance. The secret of these pistols lay in the ammunition, which made use of an idea pioneered in the USA in the 1960s on the basis of patents granted in the early years of the twentieth centu-

ry. The special thick-wall cartridge case contains a small metal piston above a greatly reduced charge, in addition to a standard projectile. When the gun is fired, the piston thrusts the projectile into the bore, but then lodges in the case neck to trap the remaining gases.

The principal differences concern projectiles. The SP-3 has a jacketed spitzer bullet in a long-mouth rimless case, whereas the SP-4 contains a short cylindrical bullet in a short-mouth rimless case. The SP-3 can penetrate 2mm steel plate at 25m and emerge with sufficient power to remain a threat.

Introduced in 1972, the MSP-2 had a block containing two super-

imposed barrels, pivoted at the muzzle above the front of the trigger guard. These could be loaded with a special two-round clip, though the tips of the bullets approached so close to the muzzle that accuracy was very poor at distances greater than 10m. A radial lever on the left side of the frame, above the grip, locked the barrel-block shut. The trigger could be set to fire either barrel, the selector being recessed in the left grip, and the cocking lever projected alongside the lower right side of the trigger guard.

The auto-loading PSS, designed by Anatoliy Levchenko, shares the 7.62mm SP-3 cartridge with the

Left: A refurbished Colt .45 M1911A1 pistol with a La France Specialities C88 sound suppressor. Note the auxiliary sights on top of the suppressor body.

about 250m/sec in air, giving an effective range of 50m. Performance ranges from an effective range of 17m in 5m-deep water to only 6m in a depth of 40m.

Experience suggested improvements, and so the SPP-1M was introduced in 1979. An additional spring above the sear eases the trigger pull, while the enlarged trigger guard admits the three-fingered 'warm equipment' diver's glove issued in arctic waters. SPP-1M pistols are 244mm long and weigh about 950gm unloaded.

The latest Soviet secret pistol, surely the ultimate of all combination weapons, is the NRS-2, or 'Special Commando (or Scout) Knife', 284mm long with a serrated-back blade measuring 162mm x 28mm. This extraordinary design is basically a multi-purpose field knife, issued with a plastic sheath doubling as a wire-cutter and a carrier which can be attached to the thigh with two buckled straps. The hilt of the knife contains a simple single-barrel pistol sharing the 7.62mm SP-4 silent cartridge with the auto-loading PSS. In normal circumstances the muzzle is covered by a waterproof pommel-cap.

Russian promotional literature has claimed that the NRS-2 'isn't only cold steel, for use in an emergency. It's not only a weapon, it's a universal instrument which can cut metal, fell a tree, crumble stone, get and cook food, mend clothes, and dismantle a vehicle.' The owner of an NRS-2 can saw through 10mm-diameter rods; cut two-core wire with core diameters as large as 2.5mm; cut telephone wires (5mm diameter); sever electrical cable carrying up to 400V; and extract screws with head diameters smaller than 6mm. Packed in its sheath, the knife measures 322mm x 65mm and weighs 620gm.

MSP-2. Production seems to have begun about 1979. The pistol is a conventional blowback with the return spring around the barrel, a self-cocking hammer-type firing mechanism, and a radial safety lever set into the left side of the slide above the back of the grip. The detachable box magazine holds six rounds. Weighing only about 850gm without its magazine, the PSS was only a little larger than the 5.45mm PSM. Performance is said to include the ability to pierce standard steel helmets at 20m, and a maximum effective range of about 50m.

A notable increase in submarine sabotage persuaded the Soviet authorities to begin work on special firearms in 1969. By 1970 Vladimir Simonov had perfected the 4.5mm SPP-1, and this silenced underwater pistol was formally approved in March 1971. A non-detachable block of four barrels could be loaded with four-round clips and fired with the aid of a self-cocking mechanism which struck the primers sequentially.

The unique 4.5mm SP-2 cartridge consists of an attenuated dart-like steel projectile loaded into a tapered rimmed case with a slight neck. Loaded cartridges are about 145mm overall and weigh 18gm, 13.2gm being contributed by the 115mm dart. Muzzle velocity is

MISCELLANEOUS HANDGUNS

AIR GUNS

Among the most deadly of all pre-1800 secret handguns ˙were reservoir-type airguns, introduced in the seventeenth century. Although they were often very large and difficult to conceal, they were effective silent killers.

The oldest air pistols known to survive are a pair made in Saxony in the middle of the seventeenth century by gunsmith Georg Fehr of Dresden. Now in the Tøjhusmuseet collection in Copenhagen, they are unwieldy, with air reservoirs concentric with the barrel.

By the middle of the eighteenth century, the barrel-reservoir pistol had been superseded by butt- and ball-reservoir patterns. Although these were invariably long arms (the heavy reservoir was a particularly clumsy fitting on a pistol), a few handguns were made. Yet even these were usually accompanied by detachable shoulder stocks.

Ball-reservoir guns were particularly popular in Britain in the last quarter of the eighteenth century, the pistols often being facsimiles of the elegant duelling pistols of the day. Their quality was usually high, and the use of silver mounts often dates construction accurately. A typical mock-flintlock example by Edward Bate of London (active 1763–c.1810) has silver mounts hallmarked for 1787/8; another, by Joseph Davidson of London, owned by Glasgow Art Gallery and Museum, is hallmarked for 1796/7. The latter gun is signed *Jph. Davidson – Borough London*, and the mounts show the mark of the renowned silversmith Moses Brent.

Butt-reservoir guns were also popular in Europe. A mid-eighteenth-century example by Samuel Kühlmann of Breslau was once owned by the Berlin Zeughaus, and an inventory taken on the death in 1768 of Landgraf Ludwig VIII of Hesse-Darmstadt included four pairs of air pistols.

Magazine-feed air pistols existed in small numbers. At least one was made by 'Bouillet à Paris', dating it later than 1767, when the gunsmith moved to the French capital city from Saint-Étienne. The most popular system was developed by the Tirolese gunsmith Bartolomeo Girandoni shortly before 1780, forming the basis for a sharpshooter's rifle briefly issued in the Austrian army. Balls from a tube magazine alongside the barrel were fed into the breech by the lateral movement of a spring-loaded block. The Girandoni system was fashionable in Viennese circles in the first quarter of the nineteenth century. Philip Colnot, Josef Contriner, Josef Früwirth, Josef Oesterlein, Ignaz Sender and Friedrich Stützinger all made guns of this type. Stormer of Herzberg made them in Germany, and in Britain smiths as diverse as Staudenmayer of London, Hanson of Huddersfield, and Cantelo of Newport (Isle of Wight) became involved.

The Metropolitan Museum in New York once owned a pair of air pistols with the tube magazines beneath the barrel and feed-blocks which moved vertically; these are believed to be Austrian, but are not signed.

Alternative breech-loading solutions were also tried. An air pistol made in 1792 for the king of Sweden, probably in Germany, had a cylindrical breech block which rotated around a transverse axis. The ball was placed in a recess in the top surface of the block when the action was opened; the block was then closed to form an extension of the bore and so connect a long narrow transfer port with the air reservoir.

Reservoir-type airguns gradually lost favour after 1825, as they often required 1,000 strokes of an air pump to charge them. The reservoirs were prone to rupture if pressure rose too far, and fatal accidents were common. Guns of reservoir type were superseded for sporting use by the bellows-gun, which had origins in the sixteenth century. However, owing to the limitations of the operating system, guns of this type are almost always long arms. A few 'bellows pistols' were made, but they offered too little power to be useful.

The modern air gun has never enjoyed real success as an assassination weapon, though it has been popular with novelists; the simpler blow-gun/poison-dart combination has a far better record. Yet the reservoir guns were quite powerful enough to inflict a fatal wound at short range, and their reputation was sufficient to persuade many lawmakers to ban them. The penalties for carrying airguns were often extremely severe. Napoleon Bonaparte was so fearful of the Girandoni rifles issued to the Tirolese sharpshooters of the Austrian army that he ordered prisoners to be summarily executed if they were found to be armed with the 'silent killers'.

The principle of reservoir guns has been revived periodically, most recently when suitable weapons were developed for the SOE and OSS during the Second World War, but has never regained its eighteenth-century popularity.

'SCHEINTOD' GUNS

In addition to the projectile-firing 'secret weapons' designed to kill or maim, there have been several classes of non-lethal 'disabling guns'. The best-known of these are the Scheintod or 'simulated death' patterns, mostly made in Germany. Guns of this type originated at the end of the nineteenth century, accompanying the rise of bicy-

Below: Typical Scheintod pistols, from the A. L. Frank ('ALFA') catalogue of 1911.

cling. Cyclists in urban and rural areas alike soon realised that they needed some protection against dogs and wolves. One result was the small-calibre Puppy and Velo-Dog revolvers, but the availability of firearms was increasingly restricted by governments desperate to curtail uses which social reform was making increasingly unacceptable. The Scheintod guns fired blanks, flares or tear-gas cartridges; some ammunition was even loaded with charges of pepper or sand. The calibre was customarily 12mm before the First World War, though 10mm versions were also made; post-1918 guns may chamber cartridges as small as 6mm. Effectiveness depended largely on the capacity of the cartridge cases, which limited the utility of the smallest designs. This was particularly true of the tear-gas loadings and flares.

Most of the guns seem to have been marketed by Adolf Niemeyer of Suhl, to whom the brandnames DIKI-DIKI, NICO and SCHEINTOD

can probably be attributed. Trademarks of a dancing skeleton and an elephant will also be found, while many barrels will bear marks such as LEUCHTPISTOLE ('flare pistol'), NUR FÜR LEUCHTPATRONE 12M/M ('for 12mm flare-cartridges only') or FÜR GASPATRONEN ('for tear-gas cartridges'). German-made guns are usually identifiable by their crown/crown/'U' proof marks, and often by D.R.G.M. – *Deutsches Reichs Gebrauchs-Muster*, 'Imperial German registered design' – or much more rarely D.R.W.Z. for *Deutsches Reichs Waren-Zeichen*, 'Imperial German trademark'.

At their crudest, Scheintod pistols consisted of a barrel which either screwed into the breech face or was attached by a bayonet joint. More sophisticated designs could have sliding barrels locked by radial levers, but almost all had simple single-action lockwork and sheath triggers. The flare pistols marked ENTLARVT ('flash', 8mm–12mm calibre) are generally comparable.

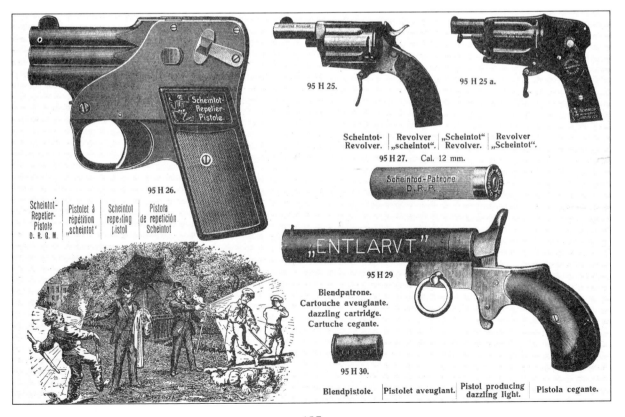

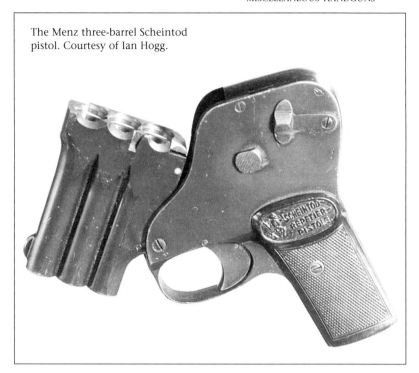

The Menz three-barrel Scheintod pistol. Courtesy of Ian Hogg.

The earliest examples, usually made before the First World War, had steel barrels and gutta-percha grips; post-war guns often had zinc barrels and bakelite grips.

The best of Niemeyer's guns included pocket revolvers, usually purchased in Belgium from manufacturers such as Rongé or Henrion, Dassy & Heuschen (Manufacture d'Armes 'HDH'). Belgian proof marks, stub-barrels, elongated cylinders and folding triggers distinguish them.

The most interesting of the Scheintods was a three-barrel pistol with a barrel block which tipped down to load. This was undoubtedly made in Suhl by August Menz, as it duplicated Menz's 'Regnum' four-barrel cartridge pistol. Most examples are marked SCHEINTOD/REPETIER-PISTOLE/D.R.G.M. on the left side of the frame above the trigger, with the NICO-and-star medallion set into the grips. They were introduced some time prior to 1911, appearing in the catalogue published by A. L. Frank of Hamburg, and were still being offered in the Glaser catalogue of 1933. Whether they were still being made by this time is not known.

The 'Nico', made in small numbers in the early 1920s, was a simplification of the Regnum-type Scheintod. It was made entirely of aluminium, with two (rare) or three-barrel blocks which could be lifted up and out of the frame when the catch on the left side of the frame was pressed downward. Two basic types were made, one with a conventional trigger guard and a guardless pattern with a special short frame.

Niemeyer seems to have stopped trading in the mid 1930s, but the principle of the Scheintod pistol was good enough to survive. The major manufacturer during the Third Reich was Bernhard Paatz of Zella-Mehlis, whose products were usually identified by the brand-name PERPLEX and a 'BP' monogram. These guns were always regarded separately from the starting-pistol type of blank firer.

The Perplex Model 1 had an external hammer and a single tipping barrel, locked by a press-button on the left side of the frame above the sheath trigger. The Model 2, usually marked D.R.P.a. ('application made for German patent'), had two superimposed barrels, an automatic ejector actuated by a spur projecting from the frame, a folding trigger, and enclosed-hammer lockwork. The earliest examples retained the push-button catch of the Model 1, but this was soon replaced by a slider.

Another German manufacturer, 'FZ' (Fritz Zink of Suhl?), made two-shot tipping-barrel Scheintod pistols styled after conventional pocket automatics. The barrels are locked with a sliding catch on the left side of the frame, and are usually marked D.R.G.M. Another manufacturer, as yet unidentified, made guns under the KNOCK-OUT brand. The simplest of these consists simply of a bayonet-joint barrel attached to a frame embedded in an enveloping wooden handgrip; the most sophisticated was a two-shot pattern with a tipping barrel block and a release button doubling as a safety catch. Knock-Out guns are usually marked GES. GESCH. or GES. GESCHÜTZT ('Protected design').

Moritz & Gerstenberger of Zella-Mehlis made gas pistols on the basis of their EM-GE branded blank-firers. The 6mm Model 3A had a tipping two-barrel block, controlled by a slider on top of the frame, and a distinctive double-trigger system. The 6mm Model 2A took the form of a small automatic, though it had to be re-cocked manually after each of its six shots. The Model 5 was a sophisticated two-shot tipping-barrel design which could handle .320 blanks and tear-gas cartridges interchangeably. Moritz & Gerstenberger may also have been responsible for the 'Stop', a propelling pencil capable of firing a single .320 blank or gas cartridge when required.

Guns chambered for tear-gas and flare ammunition are still being made in quantity – notably in Germany, where Reck, Röhm, Em-Ge and others are still active. Some have even been sold inside dummy books.

INDEX
AND BRANDNAME
DIRECTORY